34134 00287924 2

Leabharlainn nan E

D0492992

BERRIES

Delicious, nutritious and good for you

BERRIES

Delicious, nutritious
and good for you

Lee Faber

Abbeydale Press

© Copyright 2008 Bookmart Limited

All rights reserved.
No part of this publication may be reproduced, stored
in a retrieval system or transmitted by any means,
electronic, mechanical, photocopying or otherwise,
without the prior permission in writing
of the publisher.

ISBN 978-1-86147-240-3

1 3 5 7 9 10 8 6 4 2

Published by Abbeydale Press
an imprint of Bookmart Ltd
Registered number 2372865
Trading as Bookmart Ltd
Blaby Road, Wigston, Leicester
LE18 4SE, England

Produced by Omnipress Limited, UK
Illustrations by Tegan Sharrard
Cover design by Omnipress Limited

Printed in Dubai

ABOUT THE AUTHOR

Lee Faber is a native-born American who became a British
citizen, having been in the UK since 1981. She has lived and
worked in New York, Florida, London and now resides in
Wiltshire.

During her career she has been involved in book editing and
writing with an emphasis on health, food and cookery. She has
specialised in Americanising/Anglicising books on a variety of
subjects for both US and UK publishers.

She is an accomplished cook and has created many recipes.

CONTENTS

Introduction

Wild berries have been gathered and eaten since prehistoric times. While men were the principal hunters, women were mostly gatherers. They looked primarily for edible roots, green plants, nuts and berries. Over time, they discovered what was edible and what was not.

The advent of agriculture was probably an accident which occurred when gatherers, coming home in the spring, realised that the seeds they had dropped were now plants, providing much more food.

Plants and berries are still very important foods. Berries seem to be in the news every day, it seems that everyone is trying to get onto the health bandwagon by claiming that their berries are higher in vitamins, antioxidants and anthocyanins (the darker the berry, the healthier it is supposed to be).

While many of the berries mentioned in this book have been used by food and drink processors for years, there is now global emphasis in the research and development departments of major flavour, fragrance, food ingredient and pharmaceutical companies to establish novel extraction processes and new applications for their many useful components. There is increasing demand from the cosmetic industry, as well as from food manufacturers, for effective nature-derived raw materials.

This book will only touch on a few of these applications: there is enough activity in these areas to fill another book!

There is no doubt that berries are good for you and that eating them is a very pleasant way to achieve the famous five a day. But in a way, I think we've lost the plot. Will they cure cancers, diabetes, heart disease? Will they help us to lose weight? Reduce cholesterol? Probably not. But they can treat the symptoms of some diseases and might even prevent some illnesses. Are they an important part of healthy eating? Yes, I believe they are. So instead of looking for the 'perfect superfood', I think we should focus on how delicious berries are and just enjoy them for their taste and the healthy benefits that they bring us.

There are many wonderful, luscious berries. But there are also some poisonous ones. Care should be taken when eating unfamiliar berries. By the time you swallow, it may be too late. This is a book about berries — their history, how to pick them, how to store them, how to eat them, their health attributes and recipes that utilise those juicy fruits that grow wild and those that you can cultivate.

But What is a Berry?

In botanical terms, a berry is the most common type of simple fleshy fruit; a fruit in which the entire ovary wall ripens into an edible pericarp, (the dictionary defines pericarp as fruit wall, but in layman's terms it consists of the stone or pips, the fruit you eat and the skin). The flowers of these 'real' berry plants have a superior ovary and have one or more carpels (one of the structural units of a pistil, representing a modified ovule-bearing leaf) within a thin covering and fleshy interiors. The seeds are embedded in the common flesh of the ovary.

In this sense, the tomato is a berry and the strawberry is not. Other examples of botanical berries include the grape, date, avocado, persimmon, aubergine, guava, ground cherry and chilli pepper. Citrus fruit such as oranges and lemons, are modified berries called 'hesperidia'. The fruit of cucumbers and melons are modified berries called 'pepos'.

In common parlance, the term 'berry' refers generically to any small, sweet fruit; in this sense, the strawberry is a berry and the tomato is not. Other berries in this, but not the botanical, sense include aggregate fruits such as the blackberry, the raspberry and the boysenberry. In this book we will discuss only those fruits generally accepted as being 'berries', regardless of their botanical associations.

These fruits tend to be small, sweet, juicy and brightly coloured, contrasting with their background to make them more attractive to animals who disperse them and thus scatter widely the seeds of the plant.

Most berries are edible, but some are poisonous. There are no rules for distinguishing poisonous from edible types. Those wishing to harvest wild berries must familiarise themselves with species in their area and learn how to prepare them.

Common Cultivated Berries

BLACKBERRIES

Blackberries are in the same botanical family as roses and are closely related to strawberries. They are native to most temperate regions of the world, i.e., Europe, parts of North and South America, Australia and Asia.

The first time I ever saw blackberries outside of a supermarket was in the garden of a home I had recently moved into, trailing over a fence shared by a neighbour. Having asked permission to pick them, I armed myself with a bucket. Somehow, the most succulent-looking ones were just out of reach, but there were plenty of others to choose from. It was only later that I realised just how similar blackberries are to roses, because I had scratches all over my bare arms due to the thorns. However, no blackberries will ever taste as good to me as the ones I picked that day!

References have been made to blackberries as far back as 400 BC. Historically, blackberries were valued not only as a food source, but also as a medicine. Blackberry juice was used to treat infections and the bark and leaves were dried and pounded as a remedy for dysentery. In the UK, blackberries and honey were traditionally used as a cure for sore throats and chest colds and navy blue and indigo dyes were originally made from blackberry juice.

Commercially, blackberries were first cultivated in Europe in the 17th century. They are now grown in Europe, Asia, New Zealand and North America, with Oregon in the US the 'blackberry centre of the world' producing over 6,000 acres (2425 hectares). There are several different types of blackberry grown in Oregon, including 'Marion', 'Boysen' and 'Logan'. Other American cultivators include Washington State, British Columbia, California, Mexico, Guatemala, Costa Rica and Chile.

Blackberries that are abundant in the UK at the height of the summer should be picked in the morning, before the summer sun causes them to grow soft. The blackberry must be just about the most picked wild fruit in the country. For some reason, even children like doing it! They are never far away from you, either around wasteland or roadsides, plus there's ample to share with birds and insects. Blackberries will not ripen off the bush, so pick only those that are plump and black and easily pull away from their stems. After picking, keep them cool and dry to discourage mould. Don't pick them after the first of October, though — the old wives tale is that 'Old Nick' gets to them then. If you are buying blackberries, don't buy any punnets with juice leaking out of them as this is a sign of an overripe berry.

Store blackberries unwashed and uncovered in the refrigerator in a shallow bowl lined with kitchen paper, where they will keep for a few days. Rinse them just before using. Blackberries should be served at room temperature for the fullest flavour.

Blackberries are great for crumbles, pies and jam, especially when mixed with their natural partner, apples. They also make wonderful ice creams and frozen desserts (see Berry Recipes, page 97). Of course, to get the best out of the vitamins C and E, eat them raw.

To freeze, rinse the berries, drain thoroughly and transfer in a single layer to a baking tray lined with kitchen paper. Place the baking tray in the freezer until the berries are frozen. They can then be stored in airtight freezer bags for up to two years.

BLUEBERRIES

They are blue, bursting with goodness and quickly becoming very popular as a new cash crop for British farmers as they gear up to supply the great demand for this new 'superfood'. Ever since 2005, when a bunch of health studies revealed the beneficial antioxidant and other health-giving properties of what was previously regarded as a pie filling, the blueberry has become Britain's most fashionable fruit. Sales are rocketing and supermarkets are encouraging British farmers to grow them. In Europe, the key blueberry growers are Spain, Holland and Belgium, but the UK market is growing as more and more Britons are discovering their versatility. The hasn't seen many British blueberries yet, because, as a crop, they take up to two years to establish, only reaching full harvest in years four and five, but the crop can apparently last for 10–20 years, making it a good investment.

Blueberries are members of the heath family (*Ericaceae*) and are related to cranberries. Also known as bilberries, whortleberries and hurtleberries, and sometimes confused with huckleberries, they are named for their velvety, deep-blue colour, of course. These luscious berries are one of the few fruits native to North America.

When it comes to history, the blueberry has very little. The oldest blueberry plantation in the UK dates back to 1959. Even in their native North America, blueberries have only been cultivated for 100 years.

The first commercial blueberries in the US were established in New Jersey from seedlings collected from the Native Americans, who were very fond of wild blueberries. As well as eating them fresh and sun-dried in sweet preparations, native tribes used blueberries to make pemmican — a mixture of minced air-dried meat, fat and berries. They also used the berries, leaves and roots for medicinal purposes and as a fabric dye.

Blueberries used to be picked by hand until the invention of the blueberry rake by Abijah Tabbutt of Maine in 1822, so it's no wonder that Maine's state berry is the blueberry.

The most popular variety of blueberry is *Vaccinium corymbosum*, known as the 'highbush' or 'cultivated' blueberry. 'Cultivated' blueberries are larger and sweeter than 'wild' blueberries. Blueberries demand acidic soil and are happy in well-irrigated sandy areas. The dozen or so UK growers are clustered around coastal areas such as Dorset, Norfolk and Suffolk. The wild 'lowbush' varieties, e.g., *Vaccinium augustifolium* are a favourite of those who like to pick their own.

These indigo-blue pellets are not entirely unknown to the UK. Related to the blueberry is the bilberry (known as a blaeberry in Scotland), a smaller-berried wild plant that grows abundantly on heaths and moors. Given their diminutive size, these wild berries are not the easiest to pick, but their flavour is superb.

Twenty years ago, one could barely find blueberries at any price in the UK; today they are probably as popular as strawberries. In 2007, substantial quantities of British blueberries were available in supermarkets in July and August. Before now, blueberries originated from Chile and the US. Growers have been busy preparing for the first sizeable blueberry crop, with the bushes now matured and bearing fruit. This year I also saw supermarket and fruiterer berries from Canada and Argentina.

When buying blueberries, select berries that are completely blue, with no tinge of red. That natural shimmery silver coating you see on blueberries is desirable, as it is a natural protectant.

Blueberries must be ripe when purchased, as they do not continue to ripen after harvesting. Avoid soft, watery or mouldy blueberries. Stained or leaking containers are an indication of fruit past its prime.

Keep blueberries refrigerated, unwashed, in a rigid container covered with cling film. They should last up to two weeks if they are freshly-picked. Water on fresh blueberries hastens deterioration, so do not wash before refrigerating.

To freeze, first rinse, then drain thoroughly. Transfer to a baking tray lined with kitchen paper and pat dry. Pick over and discard immature or overripe berries. Place the baking tray in the freezer until the berries are frozen. They can then be stored in airtight freezer bags for up to one year. These berries will not stick together when frozen.

CRANBERRIES

Some say the name cranberry comes from the berries being a favourite food of cranes. Others maintain the name is derived from 'craneberry' because, before the flower expands, the stem, calyx and petals resemble the neck, head and bill of a crane. An old English name is 'fenberry', because they were grown in fen (marsh) lands.

Cranberries have been eaten by Arctic peoples for millennia, and they remain a very popular fruit for wild harvesting in the Nordic countries and Russia. They were formerly wild harvested in Scotland, but the plants have now become too scarce. The first record of cranberry consumption comes from the analysis of a mug in a Bronze Age tomb in Denmark which contained the remains of a fermented drink made from wild cranberries, grain and myrtle.

Native Americans were the first to use cranberries as a source of food. They are reported to have introduced the cranberry (*Viburnum edule*) to starving English settlers in Massachusetts c. 1620, who incorporated the berry into their traditional Thanksgiving feast. The colonists not only learned how to harvest and cook the cranberries from the natives, they discovered a new use for them – cleaning silverware. When silver items were boiled in their acidic juice, they removed tarnish! Cranberries are frequently served as a compote or jelly, known generically as 'cranberry sauce' (either the wobbly jelly that comes out of a tin or something similar to relish). Cranberry sauce is still widely regarded as an indispensable part of a traditional American and Canadian Thanksgiving menu. The berry is also used in baking muffins, scones, cakes and biscuits, but unlike many other berries, are normally considered too tart to be eaten raw, out of hand.

Cranberry juice, another very popular product, is usually sweetened to reduce its natural severe sharpness, or blended with other fruit juices, such as passion fruit, raspberry or blueberry.

The fruit of the cranberry shrub is initially white, but turns a deep red when fully ripe. White cranberry juice, with a smoother, milder flavour, is a new addition to supermarket shelves. Cranberries are a major commercial crop in some US states and Canadian provinces. Most cranberries are processed into products such as juice, sauce and sweetened dried cranberries, with the remainder sold fresh to consumers in the autumn.

Fresh cranberries can be frozen at home and will keep up to nine months; they can be used directly in recipes without thawing.

Dried cranberries, sometimes called 'craisins', have become very popular and are a tasty alternative to raisins. They are an excellent addition to either dry or cooked cereals, and also a tasty snack by themselves any time of the day.

Most dried cranberries, particularly those marketed by large-scale manufacturers, do contain added sugar, because most people find dried cranberries without sugar a little too tart. However, home drying methods can create these tart little morsels, which are excellent for use in sweeter baked goods.

Some dried cranberries may also be coated in vegetable oil, to prevent them from sticking together, but the same effect can be achieved by shaking them in a plastic bag containing a little flour.

An average fresh cup of cranberries contains about 50 calories. Dried cranberries, on the other hand, have over 300 calories per cup. Part of this has to do with the number of berries. Naturally one can fit more dried berries into a cup than fresh berries. The additional calories also come from added sugar.

Dried cranberries do tend to offer a higher amount of dietary fibre; about 7 grams of fibre per cup. Fresh berries only yield about 4 grams. However, if one were to eat two cups of fresh cranberries, one would still only consume one-third of the calories, while getting 8 grams of fibre. But most people do not eat raw cranberries because they are very sour.

While dried cranberries do not have the vitamin content of fresh berries, they are a nice change from raisins and they seem to be a favourite with children. A child who detests salad may change his or her mind when offered a green salad containing dried cranberries and raspberry vinaigrette (see page 136).

CURRANTS

Currants come in three colours — black, red and white, with blackcurrant the absolute winning choice of British children.

BLACKCURRANTS

The blackcurrant (*Ribes nigrum*) is a species of Ribes berry native to central and northern Europe and northern Asia. In French it is called 'cassis'.

Recently, scientists have claimed that the darker the berry the healthier it is, and it is now said that our humble blackcurrant is healthier than blueberries or, the most recent fad, goji berries. In addition to their other health-giving properties, blackcurrants also contain a very high level of vitamin C.

Blackcurrants were first mentioned in England during medieval times, when they were used to flavour wine. Imported from Holland, they were slow to catch on and not as popular as redcurrants. By the 16th century they were being grown in gardens for food in France, but did not become popular until the 18th century, when they became accepted as a food and medicinal plant.

In England the juice was boiled with sugar as a treatment for sore throats (and is still a very popular flavouring for sore throat pastilles). By the 19th century, commercial cassis liqueur production was underway, making the fruit even more popular.

During World War II most fruits rich in vitamin C, such as oranges, became almost impossible to obtain in the UK. Since blackcurrant berries are a rich source of vitamin C and blackcurrant plants are suitable for growing in the UK climate, blackcurrant cultivation was encouraged by the British government. Soon the yield of the nation's crop increased significantly. From 1942 onwards, almost the entire British blackcurrant crop was made into blackcurrant syrup (or cordial) and distributed to the nation's children free of charge, giving rise to the lasting popularity of blackcurrant flavourings in Britain.

Blackcurrants were once popular in the US as well, but they became extremely rare in the 20th century after currant farming was banned in the early 1900s. The ban was enacted when it was discovered that blackcurrants helped to spread the tree disease White Pine Blister Rust, which was thought to threaten the then-booming US lumber industry.

Blackcurrants have a very sweet and sharp taste. They are made into jelly, jam, juice, ice cream, cordial and liqueur. In the UK, Europe and Commonwealth countries, some types of confectionery include a blackcurrant flavour, but this is generally missing in the US, even within the same brand. Instead grape flavour in sweets (including grape jelly) almost mirrors the use of blackcurrant in both its ubiquity in the US, and its rarity on the eastern side of the Atlantic.

In Russia, it is common to infuse slightly sweetened vodka with blackcurrant leaves, making a deep yellowish-green beverage with a sharp flavour and an astringent taste. Blackcurrant berries can also be used to flavour vodka. In the UK, blackcurrant juice is often mixed with cider to make a popular drink called 'Cider and Black'. It is also believed that adding a small amount of blackcurrant to Guinness will bring out a sweeter taste in the beer, making it a better beverage in some beer drinkers' opinions (and making some other Guinness drinkers cringe!).

In addition to being juiced and used in jellies, syrups and cordials, blackcurrants are used in cooking. Their astringent nature brings out the flavour in many sauces and meat dishes and they are also popular in desserts. It was once thought that currants needed to be 'topped and tailed' (the stalk and flower remnants removed) before cooking. This is not the case, as these parts are easily assimilated during the cooking process. If one prefers to do this, however, the blackcurrants can first be frozen, then shaken vigorously. The tops and tails will break off and can be separated easily from the fruit. Blackcurrants are more tart and intensely flavoured than redcurrants and are normally cooked. Their high pectin level means that they also set very well and make lovely jam (see my friend Arina's recipe, page 108).

Unlike some other berries, blackcurrants can remain on the bush for up to two weeks after they are ripe without deteriorating. If you are picking them off the bush, the clusters of fruit easily lift off when ripe.

When buying blackcurrants, only buy berries that are plump and firm with solid-colour shiny skin. Do not purchase any with cracks or brown spots.

Store the berry clusters unwashed and uncovered in a single layer on kitchen paper in the refrigerator for three to four days. Before using, remove the fruit from the stalk either with a fork held upside-down or your fingers and rinse and drain.

To freeze, rinse and drain thoroughly, then transfer to a baking tray lined with kitchen paper and pat dry. Discard immature or overripe berries. Place the baking tray in the freezer until the berries are frozen. They can then be stored in airtight freezer bags for up to one year.

REDCURRANTS
The redcurrant (*Ribes rubrum*) is a member of the gooseberry family. They are rich in vitamin C, iron and potassium.

Redcurrants first appeared in history around the 15th century, when they were described as herbs, with no mention of any culinary application. In 1629, the apothecary to King James I wrote that redcurrants were usually eaten fresh in summer or made into preserves in the winter. One 19th-century horticulturalist noted how to store redcurrants so they would keep for years in corked bottles: 'if they are gathered perfectly dry and not too ripe, and as long as they are stored away from air in a dry environment, packed into a bottle and corked and the bottle is stored cork-side down in a chest and the space around them filled with sand, this would ensure their longest keeping'.

When planted, redcurrants form into beautiful clumps of ripe fruit and are perfect for jellies, juices and as flavouring for savoury dishes such as game and lamb. It is worth buying a couple of young plants as they really are easy to grow. Some sunlight is preferred to help sweeten the berries, but they will grow happily in most sites. There is usually no problem with pests other than hungry birds, who absolutely love the berries. A fruit cage is the best way of protecting your crops and they need protecting, because a good batch of fruits will be required to make a worthwhile jelly.

Modern redcurrant cultivars have the ability to ripen all the berries on a stem simultaneously. The fruit turns red before it is ripe, so leave them on the bush for one to two weeks after developing their colour to ripen completely. As with blackcurrants, redcurrants can stay on the bush for up to two weeks after they are ripe without deteriorating. If you are picking them off the bush, the clusters of fruit easily lift off the bush when ripe.

When buying redcurrants, only buy berries that are plump and firm with solid-colour shiny skin. Do not purchase any with cracks or brown spots.

Store the berry clusters unwashed and uncovered in a single layer on kitchen paper in the refrigerator for three to four days. Before using, remove the fruit from the stalk either with a fork held upside-down or your fingers and rinse and drain.

To freeze, rinse and drain thoroughly, then transfer to a baking tray lined with kitchen paper and pat dry. Discard immature or overripe berries. Place the baking tray in the freezer until the berries are frozen. They can then be stored in airtight freezer bags for up to one year. Freezing will detach them from their stalks, which can easily be discarded when you thaw the berries.

Redcurrants are wonderful made into a sorbet, just warmed through a light game gravy or meat sauce, or added to a casserole of venison or roast goose just before serving. They can also be frosted with egg white and caster sugar and used as a decoration for puddings or cocktails, but best of all is as a jelly with hot or cold cuts of roast lamb and other meats.

WHITECURRANTS

Whitecurrants, sometimes referred to as white currants, (*Ribes sativum*) are beautiful, luminous berries and the sweetest of the three varieties, providing a juicy sweet flavour for a variety of foods. The berries of the whitecurrant are most often used for desserts, summer salads and soups, succulent sauces for poultry or pork, sweet or tart jams or sorbets, homemade wines and eaten fresh, out of hand, since they have a sweeter taste.

In a poem by Amy Lowell (1874–1925) from *What's O'Clock*, she wrote:

Shall I give you white currants?
I do not know why, but I have a sudden fancy for this
    fruit.
At the moment, the idea of them cherishes my senses,
And they seem more desirable than flawless emeralds.
Since I am, in fact, empty-handed,
I might have chosen gems out of India,
But I choose white currants.
Is it because the raucous wind is hurtling round the
    house-corners?
I see it with curled lips and stripped fangs, gaunt and
    haunting energy,
Come to snout, and nibble, and kill the little crocus roots.
Shall we call it white currants?
You may consider it as a symbol if you please.
You may find them tart, or sweet, or merely agreeable in
    colour,
So long as you accept them,
And me.

ELDERBERRIES

Elder or Elderberry (*Sambucus*) is a genus of between 5–30 species of shrubs or small trees formerly thought to be in the honeysuckle family, but now shown by genetic evidence to be correctly classified in the moschatel (muskroot) family. The genus is native to temperate and subtropical regions of both the northern and southern hemispheres; the elder is more widespread in the northern hemisphere, with southern hemisphere occurrence restricted to parts of Australasia and South America.

Both flowers and berries can be made into elderberry wine, and in Hungary an elderberry brandy is produced (requiring 50 kg of fruit to produce 1 litre of brandy!). The alcoholic drink Sambuca is made by infusing elderberries and anise into alcohol. The berries are best not eaten raw as they are mildly poisonous, causing vomiting, particularly if eaten unripe. The mild cyanide toxicity is destroyed by cooking. The berries can also be made into jam, pies or Pontack sauce (see Berry Recipes, page 123). All green parts of the plant are poisonous, containing cyanogenic glycosides.

Elderflowers may be used to make a herbal tea, which is believed to be a remedy for colds and fever. In Europe, the flowers are made into a syrup or cordial which is diluted with water before drinking. The popularity of this traditional drink has recently encouraged some commercial soft-drink producers to introduce elderflower-flavoured drinks. The flowers can also be used to make a mildly alcoholic, sparkling elderflower 'champagne'.

The elder was formerly thought to be unlucky to have in the garden. If an elder tree was cut down, a spirit known as the 'Elder Mother' would be released and take her revenge; shown in one way by a poem known as the *Wiccan Rede* where one line reads:

Elder be the Lady's tree, burn it not or cursed you'll be.

This is probably derived from ancient pagan beliefs, which held the elder sacred to the Moon Goddess.

The tree could only safely be cut while chanting a rhyme to the Elder Mother.

In *Monty Python and the Holy Grail*, John Cleese's character, The Frenchman, says, 'Your mother was a hamster and your father smelled of elderberries'!

For those who haven't been around elderberries, some people think that the odour of elderberries is similar to urine.

Elderberries are only edible when cooked. They can be used like blueberries in pies, muffins, pancakes, teas and an abundance of other things. If vinegar or pectin and plenty of sugar are added, they make good jam and jelly. A lot of people overlook this fruit thinking it's for winemaking only and this is borne out by it once being called the 'Englishman's Grape'.

The ancient Egyptians discovered that applying elderberry flowers to the skin improved the complexion and healed burns. All parts of the elder have long enjoyed a strong medicinal reputation on their own merits, however, ONLY the berries and flowers are recommended for internal use today.

In fact, elderberries contain more vitamin C than any other herb, except for blackcurrants and rosehips!

To store elderberries after picking, follow the same method as for currants (page 20).

To freeze elderberries, sort and wash them and package according to one of the following methods.

Dry pack, no sugar: pack into containers, leaving 1 cm (½-inch) headspace. Seal and freeze. This method is generally used when the berries are used in cooked dishes.

Wet pack, in syrup: pack into containers and cover with syrup, leaving 1 cm (½-inch) headspace. Seal and freeze. A medium syrup is made by dissolving 675 g (1½ lb) of

sugar in 900 ml (1½ pints) of water, to yield about
1 litre (1¾ pints) of syrup. Chill before using.

GOOSEBERRIES

Gooseberries are derived mostly from two species: the
European gooseberry (*Ribes grossularia*), native to the
Caucasus Mountains and North Africa; and the American
gooseberry (*Ribes hirtellum*), native to the north-eastern
and north-central US and adjacent parts of Canada. So-
called European cultivars are pure species, but virtually
all American cultivars also have European genes.

The fruit, borne singly or in pairs at the axils, is a berry
with many minute seeds at the centre. A gooseberry may
be green, white (grey-green), yellow, or shades of red
from pink to purple to almost black. Fruits of the
European gooseberry may be very large, like a small
plum, but are usually 2.5 cm (1 inch) long, less in width.
American gooseberry fruits are smaller, about 1 cm (up to
½ inch), perfectly round, all becoming pink to wine-red
at maturity. Skin colour is most intense in full sunlight.
Berries generally drop when overripe. The fruit has a
flavour all of its own; the best dessert cultivars as
luscious as the best apple, strawberry or grape.

The British climate is particularly well-suited to
producing perfect gooseberries — juicy, tart and full-
flavoured — and over the years they have captured the
hearts of Britons more than any other nationality.

The gooseberry season starts with the familiar striped
green gooseberries. These are the best ones for cooking.
Use them to make a delicious gooseberry fool (see the
recipe on page 126) or poach them with a little sugar and
water to make a traditional accompaniment to mackerel.
Later in the season come the red, yellow or golden-
coloured dessert gooseberries which are sweet enough to
be eaten raw. Select those with a plump, grape-like
texture.

Indigenous to cooler areas of Europe and western Asia,
gooseberries were first cultivated in Britain in the 16th
century, when they were used medicinally and

recommended to plague victims in London. They reached their peak of popularity in 19th-century Britain when gooseberry wines, pies and puddings were commonplace. Amateur gooseberry clubs, mostly in the Midlands and the north of England, held fiercely fought competitions to find the biggest and tastiest fruit, and many new varieties were developed during this period. Some of the oldest clubs still exist.

In 1905 the whole European crop of gooseberries was wiped out by a mildew disease accidentally introduced from America. The plant was reintroduced by crossing with mildew-resistant American gooseberries. Today gooseberries are grown and eaten in cooler climates across the globe, from northern America and northern Europe to the Himalayas. However, the apple has virtually replaced the gooseberry as a source of pectin. Nonetheless, we do enjoy our gooseberries in Britain.

If you are picking your own, choose berries that are ripe with well-coloured fruit in early to midsummer. Unlike currants, gooseberries can be picked as they are beginning to ripen, just as the colour starts to appear. They will develop both flavour and colour if kept in a airtight freezer bag lined with damp kitchen paper in the refrigerator. They should keep, stored this way, for several weeks. Softer dessert gooseberries are less durable; keep them refrigerated and eat within two or three days.

To prepare gooseberries for eating, peel away the husk if necessary and rinse. Pat dry and top and tail the berries with scissors.

Gooseberries also freeze well. Rinse, drain, pat dry and put into airtight freezer bags for up to one year. You do not need to thaw them before cooking. Gooseberries can vary quite a bit in sharpness; be prepared to adjust the amount of sugar specified in recipes.

Gooseberries have a refreshing, distinctive flavour and astringency similar to rhubarb, which is enhanced when they are cooked. Their tartness particularly complements game, wild duck, goose and oily fish, such as mackerel.

The children of today aren't anywhere near as innocent as they were in my generation; they know where babies come from. We really did believe that the stork delivered newborn babies by popping them under gooseberry bushes for parents to find!

RASPBERRIES

Raspberries belong to the genus *Rubus*, which is a part of the rose family. Cultivated raspberries are derived mainly from two species, the wild red raspberry (*Rubus ideaus*) and black raspberry (*Rubus occidentalis*). There are over 200 species of raspberries.

According to Greek mythology, raspberries were once all white until one day when a nymph, picking raspberries to soothe the crying baby Zeus, pricked her finger on a thorn. The nymph's blood stained the berries, and they've been a brilliant red ever since. Myths aside, today not all raspberries are red, but come in a variety of hues, from almost black to golden.

The red raspberry (*Rubus idaeus*) is indigenous to Asia Minor and North America. Fruits were gathered from the wild by the people of Troy in the foothills of Mount Ida in Turkey around the time of Christ. Records of domestication were found in 4th-century writings of Palladius, a Roman agriculturist, and seeds have been discovered at Roman forts in Britain. Therefore, the Romans are thought to have spread cultivation throughout Europe.

In medieval Europe, wild berries were considered both medicinal and utilitarian. Their juices were used in paintings and illuminated manuscripts. During this period only the rich partook of their tasty bounty. King Edward I (1272–1307) is recognised as the first person to call for the cultivation of berries. By the 17th century, British gardens were rich with berries and berry bushes. By the 18th century berry cultivation practices had spread throughout Europe.

When settlers from Europe came to America they found Native Americans already utilising and eating berries. Due to the nomadic nature of this culture, berries were dried for preservation and ease of transportation. Settlers also brought cultivated raspberries that were native to Europe with them to the new colonies.

Always pick raspberries in the morning, before the hot summer sun softens them, and when the berries are at their peak of ripeness. Raspberries differ from blackberries in that they detach from their hull when they are harvested, leaving a soft, hollow fruit that is exceptionally fragile. When a raspberry is perfectly ripe, it will be a deep red colour with a characteristic flavour and aroma and will detach from its hull at the slightest touch.

When purchasing raspberries, choose brightly coloured, fragrant, plump berries without hulls. Attached hulls are a sign that the berries were picked too early and will undoubtedly be too tart. Avoid soft, shrivelled or mouldy berries. Raspberries are very delicate and have a short shelf life in the refrigerator of 2–3 days. Store them unwashed and uncovered in a shallow container on kitchen paper. Rinse just before using.

To freeze, rinse and drain the berries thoroughly, then transfer to a baking tray lined with kitchen paper and pat dry. Place the baking tray into the freezer. When the berries are frozen, transfer to airtight freezer bags and freeze for up to one year.

Raspberries are commonly thought of for dessert, but they make an excellent addition to chicken salads or in sauces for pork or poultry such as game birds. Raspberries are delicate, so add them to cooked dishes at the very last moment. When baking with frozen raspberries, use them directly from the freezer.

When serving raspberries for dessert, about the only adornment necessary is a kiss of cream, lightly whipped or not as you choose.

ROSEHIPS
Rosehips are the cherry-sized red fruits of the rose bush left behind after the bloom has died. Although nearly all

rose bushes produce rosehips, the tastiest for eating purposes come from the *Rosa rugosa* variety. The flavour is described as fruity and spicy, much like the cranberry. Harvest the fruits after the first frost, when they become fully-coloured, but not overripe. They should yield to gentle pressure but not be soft or wrinkly. Most recipes advise removing the irritating hairy seeds before processing the fruit. This may be a myth, but it is said that when these silvery hairy seeds are ingested they irritate the digestive system and cause what the aboriginal people call 'itchy bottom disease'. When cooking with rosehips, do not use any metal pans or utensils other than stainless steel or risk discolouration of the fruit and loss of its precious vitamin C content.

Rosehips of some species, especially *Rosa canina* (Dog Rose), have been used as a source of Vitamin C. Rosehips are commonly used as a herbal tea, often blended with hibiscus and as an oil. They can also be used to make jam, jelly and marmalade. Rosehip soup (see Berry Recipes, page 143) is especially popular in Sweden.

STRAWBERRIES
Curly locks! curly locks! wilt thou be mine?
Thou shall't not wash dishes, nor yet feed the swine,
But sit on a cushion and sew a fine seam,
And feed upon strawberries, sugar, and cream!

Mother Goose Nursery Rhyme

This sounds like the height of indolence. However, our associations with strawberries are much more strenuous. Whenever I think of strawberries, I think of Wimbledon. Every year about 27,000 kilos (almost 60,000 lb) of strawberries are eaten during the Wimbledon Tennis Championships, together with 7,000 litres (over 12,300 pints) of cream. The popularity of serving strawberries with cream is legendary.

Strawberries are a variety of the rose family called *Fragaria*. They are short plants that grow sideways, spreading out runners. The ends of the plant stems swell up and redden after the flowers have been pollinated.

The actual fruit is the tiny seed embedded in the fleshy strawberry. Botanically, strawberries are therefore not berries.

The word strawberry comes from the Old English 'streowberie' or 'streawbelige'. This is probably a combination of the words strewed and berry. Strewed means scattered or spread across. Straw could have referred to the straw that was used to keep the strawberries fertile and dry. Animal dung was often mixed in with the straw.

There are also small, wild strawberries that often grow on the edges of woods (fraises du bois, or alpine strawberries). These taste and smell delicious. One of my old neighbours used to grow them in her garden and I would make any excuse to be there just so I could pick and eat some when they were ripe.

The Romans were the first to cultivate the crop, while the 14th century saw a popularity of growing strawberries in the gardens of French palaces. They were a luxury and poor children would pick them to sell to the rich.

During Shakespeare's time the playwright George Peele in his play *The Old Wives Tale*, wrote a song linking strawberries with summer and delight.

When as the rye reach to the chin,
And chopcherry, chopcherry, ripe within,
Strawberries swimming in the cream,
And schoolboys playing in the stream . . .

In those times strawberries were eaten fresh or made into a sauce to be eaten with meat. In 1874 the sugar tax was abolished and consequently sugar became cheaper. This saw a huge increase in boiling strawberries with sugar to make jam, and by the 20th century there was widespread strawberry cultivation in Kent to supply the markets of London.

Strawberries are a source of natural sugar and provide good quantities of vitamin C as well as potassium. Unfortunately, strawberries rapidly lose their vitamin C after picking.

In the UK strawberries are in season between May and September. During the rest of the year they are imported from countries such as Spain, Holland or the US. Most commonly, strawberries are grown on fruit farms and shoppers buy them in supermarkets either fresh, frozen or as jam. Many fruit farms encourage people to visit and pick their own fruit.

More than any other berry, I think, strawberries from different places and climates taste very different. To my mind, there is nothing that matches the deep flavour and aroma of the British strawberry, which, to me, tastes like summer.

When picking strawberries, it is best to harvest them in the cool mornings or evenings as the berries are highly perishable. Ideally, they should be plump and completely red.

When buying strawberries, again look for red berries with fresh-looking green caps. Store them uncovered on kitchen paper in the refrigerator for up to a week. Hull and rinse them just before using. Just pinching the green cap off produces the best-looking berries.

I have never successfully frozen whole strawberries, which tend to get very mushy when they are defrosted. However, you can purée them before freezing for future ice creams, sorbets and coulis.

Exotic Cultivated and Wild Berries

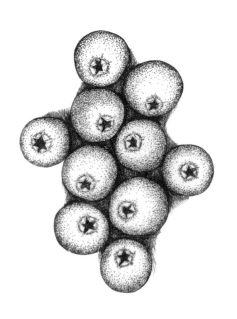

ACAI

Acai berries are the fruit of a species of palm tree, indigenous to the Amazon rainforest in Brazil. The stems, called heart of palm, are often eaten in salads.

The berries are also harvested as food. The acai berry, which is commonly pronounced *ah-sigh-ee*, is a rather small, round and purple berry. It resembles a grape or a blueberry, but is even smaller and darker. This fruit has a large seed and minimum amount of pulp. The acai berry is now widely used in energy juices, flavouring for ice cream and certain energy bars along with granola.

As acai deteriorates rapidly after harvest, its raw material is generally only available outside the immediate growing region as juice or fruit pulp that has been frozen, dried or freeze-dried. However, several companies now manufacture juices, other health drinks and sorbets made from acai berries, often in combination with other fruits.

The acai berry has a unique tropical-fruit flavour and provides a high level of nutritional benefits. It contains superior amounts of antioxidants, also known as anthocyanins. It also includes omega fatty acids, amino acids, fibre and iron, along with many other vitamins and minerals. A traditional Amazonian recipe mixes acaí fruit pulp and natural guarana seed, which gives energy and heightens mental clarity. Combined with guarana, the acai berry has an effect similar to caffeine.

Natives living in the Amazon River region in northern Brazil have eaten the acai berry as part of their diet for hundreds of years for its nutritional value. Its healing and wellness powers are legendary throughout the area. Now the popularity of the acai berry is starting to spread all over the world.

The acai berry has the following nutritional and health properties: antioxidant, antibacterial, anti-inflammatory and antimutagenic as well as being of benefit to the cardiovascular system.

Acai boasts 10 times the antioxidant benefits of grapes and twice that of blueberries.

ALLSPICE

Allspice, the dried, unripe berry of *Pimenta dioica*, an evergreen tree in the myrtle family, is the only spice grown exclusively in the western hemisphere. While there are plantations in Mexico and other parts of Central America, the finest allspice comes from Jamaica, where the climate and soil are best suited to producing the aromatic berries.

After drying, the berries are small, dark brown balls, just a little larger than peppercorns. Allspice takes its name from its aroma, which smells like a combination of spices, especially cinnamon, cloves, ginger and nutmeg.

Allspice was used by the Mayans as an embalming agent and by other South American Indians to flavour chocolate. The name 'Jamaica' comes from Xamayca, meaning 'land of wood and water' in the language of the Arawaks (the natives the Spanish encountered in the West Indies). These natives used allspice to help cure and preserve meats, sometimes animals and sometimes their enemies. The allspice-cured meat was known in Arawak as 'boucan' and so later Europeans who cured meat this way came to be known as boucaniers, which ultimately became 'buccaneers'.

In much of the world, allspice is called pimento, because the Spanish mistook the fruit for black pepper. Christopher Columbus found it during his exploration of the 'New World'. Although he was seeking pepper, he had never actually seen real pepper and he thought allspice was it. He brought it back to Spain, where it got the name 'pimienta', which is Spanish for pepper. This is especially confusing since the Spanish had already called chillies pimientos. (We can also thank the Spanish for centuries of linguistic confusion created by naming all the natives they met 'Indians'.)

The spice was imported to Europe soon after the discovery of the New World. There were several attempts made to transplant it to spice-producing regions of the east, but these trees produced little fruit. Despite its rich fragrance and strong flavour, allspice never had the same cachet in Europe as cinnamon or pepper. The English started making regular shipments to England in 1737, but by that time the lust for spices been eclipsed by other New World products like sugar and coffee. It was quite popular in England though, where it came to be known as 'English Spice'. Oddly, it's not all that popular here today, except among certain ethnic groups.

In the Napoleonic War of 1812, Russian soldiers put allspice in their boots to keep their feet warm, and the resultant improvement in odours is carried into today's cosmetic industries, where allspice berry oil is usually associated with men's toiletries (especially products with the word 'spice' on the label).

Whole dried allspice will keep indefinitely when kept out of the light in airtight jars. It can be ground in a spice mill or an electric coffee grinder. But only grind as much as you need, because the ground spice loses its flavour quickly. Allspice can be used as a substitute, measure for measure, for cinnamon, cloves or nutmeg. Conversely, to make a substitution for allspice, combine one part nutmeg with two parts each of cinnamon and cloves.

Because of its unique flavour, allspice can be used in both savoury and sweet dishes. Jerked meats like pork, chicken and goat reflect the Spanish/Jamaican background of allspice. It is a particularly popular spice in European cooking, an important ingredient in many marinades, pickling and mulling spices. Many pâtés, terrines, smoked and canned meats include allspice. A few allspice berries are added to Scandinavian pickled herring, to sauerkraut, pickles, soups, game dishes and English spiced beef. Traditionally, allspice has also been used in cakes, fruit pies, puddings, ice cream and pumpkin pie. Some Indian curries and pilaus contain allspice, and in the Middle East it is used in meat and rice dishes. It is also an ingredient in liqueurs, notably Benedictine and Chartreuse.

ARCTIC BRAMBLE

The Arctic bramble, also called arctic raspberry, *Rubus arcticus*, is a species of slow-growing bramble belonging to the rose family. Its dark-red fruit is considered a delicacy. Many consider it to be one the tastiest fruits in the world: in Russian its name is the 'berry of kings'. It grows in northern Sweden, Finland, Siberia and parts of North America. It is mainly used in liqueurs, herbal teas and juice.

BEARBERRIES

The Bearberry (*Arctostaphylos uva-ursi, Sprengel*), a small shrub, with decumbent, much branched, irregular stems and evergreen leaves, is distributed over the greater part of the northern hemisphere, being found in the northern latitudes and high mountains of Europe, Asia and America. In the UK it is common in Scotland, on heaths and barren places in hilly districts, especially in the Highlands, extending south as far as Yorkshire; it also grows on the hills of the north-west of Ireland. In America it is distributed throughout Canada and the US as far south as New Jersey and Wisconsin.

It is closely related to the Arbutus, and was formerly assigned to the same genus — in *Green's Universal Herbal*, 1832, it will be found under the name *Arbutus uva-ursi* — but it differs from Arbutus in having a smooth berry with five one-seeded stones, whereas the *Arbutus* has a rough fruit, each cell of the ovary being four- to five seeded.

The only other British species assigned to the genus, the Black Bearberry (*A. alpina*), with black berries, found on barren mountains in northern Scotland, and not at all in England, is the badge of the clan of Ross.

The generic name, derived from the Greek, and the Latin specific name, *uva-ursi*, mean the same: the 'bear's grape', and may have been given to the plant, either from the notion that bears eat the fruit with relish, or from its very rough, unpleasant flavour, which might have been considered only fit for bears.

In medicine, the only part of the bearberry that is ingested is the dried leaf, not the berry at all.

BILBERRIES

Bilberry is a name given to several species of low-growing shrubs in the genus *Vaccinium* (family *Ericaceae*) that bear tasty fruits. The species most often referred to is *Vaccinium myrtillus L.*, also known as European blueberry, blaeberry, whortleberry, whinberry (or winberry), myrtle blueberry, fraughan and probably other names regionally. They were called black-hearts in 19th-century southern England, according to Thomas Hardy's 1878 novel, *The Return of the Native*.

The word bilberry is also sometimes used in the common names of other species of the genus, including bog bilberry, bog blueberry, bog whortleberry, bog huckleberry, northern bilberry, dwarf bilberry, Cascade bilberry, mountain bilberry, black mountain huckleberry, black huckleberry, twin-leaved huckleberry, oval-leafed blueberry, oval-leaved bilberry, mountain blueberry and high-bush blueberry.

Bilberries are found in damp, acidic soils throughout the temperate and subarctic regions of the world. They are closely related to North American wild and cultivated blueberries and huckleberries in the genus *Vaccinium* and are native to northern Europe.

The easiest way to distinguish the bilberry is that it produces single or pairs of berries on the bush instead of clusters like the blueberry. Another way to differentiate it is that while blueberry fruit pulp is light green, bilberry is red or purple. In this way you can also tell the bilberry eater from the blueberry eater by his or her red fingers and lips.

Bilberries are rarely commercially cultivated, but fruits are sometimes collected from wild plants growing on publicly accessible lands, notably in Scandinavia, Scotland, Ireland and Poland. In some parts of Scandinavia it is an 'everyman's right' to collect bilberries, irrespective of land ownership. In Ireland the fruit is known as fraughan, from the Irish fraochán, and is traditionally gathered on the last Sunday in July, known as Fraughan Sunday.

Bilberries are also collected during Lúnasa, a Gaelic festival associated with the first of August. The crop of bilberries was said to indicate how well the rest of the crops would fare in their harvests later in the year.

Bilberries can be eaten fresh, but are more usually made into jams, fools, juices or pies. In France they are used as a base for liqueurs and are a popular flavouring for sorbets and other desserts. In Brittany they are often used as a flavouring for crêpes, and in the Vosges and the Massif Central areas of France, bilberry tart (tarte aux myrtilles) is the most traditional dessert.

BOYSENBERRIES

The boysenberry is a large bramble fruit, usually considered, along with the loganberry and the youngberry, a variety of blackberry (*Rubus ursinus*). The dark, reddish-black fruit is especially valued for canning and preserving. It is grown chiefly in the US, in the South and Southwest and on the Pacific Coast from southern California into Oregon.

Its flavour is somewhat reminiscent of a raspberry, with a more tart undertone, especially when the berries are not fully ripened. They are available from grocery stores and farmers' markets in the US, but since boysenberries are not very stable off the vine, it is important to eat them within two or three days of purchase.

The inventor of the boysenberry is believed to Rudolph Boysen, who experimented with various berry crosses in Napa, California, in the 1920s. In 1923, his cross of a blackberry, loganberry and raspberry successfully grew and bore fruit. The boysenberry was acquired by Walter Knott, a southern California berry farmer, who started selling the fruit commercially in 1935. Boysenberries and boysenberry preserves helped to make Knott's business famous around the state. The berry farm became America's first theme park, sited in California and now a variety of berry products are marketed by this company online to the entire US and Canada.

BUFFALO BERRIES

The buffalo berry (*Shepherdia argentea*), also called soapberry (because of its saponins, it can be substituted for soap), was named after a Canadian botanist, Dr John Shepherd. The buffalo berry grows wild throughout North America and is food for birds, bears and small mammals. It is most prevalent in the Great Plains.

Native Americans used the tart berries in various ways — as a sauce for buffalo, hence the name, pressed into cakes and smoked and used for stews and pemmican. A red dye was made from the berries and the leaves and bark were employed as medicine. The medicinal elements of buffalo berries have fallen into disuse by herbalists today. When the pioneers arrived in the US, they made the berries into jellies and jams. Another application was wine, which some people still make.

Lewis and Clark found '*great quantities of a kind of berry resembling a currant except double the size*'. The sweet fruit was '*deliciously flavored & makes delightful tarts now that the fruit is ripe*' — Clark's journal, 24 August 1804. Even though it is common to harvest the berries in July or August, buffalo berries are a tough and hardy shrub, and it is possible to pick them in some areas of the US as late as November.

Chances are you won't ever see buffalo berries because even though the plant is grown in Britain, it is basically ornamental and rarely produces fruit.

CAPE GOOSEBERRIES

Physalis peruviana (commonly known as physalis, Cape gooseberry, ground cherry, golden berry, uchuva, Inca berry or uvilla) is a species of *Physalis* indigenous to South America, but grows well in Africa. It is related to the tomato, potato and other members of the nightshade family, and closely related to the tomatillo (but not to the cherry, gooseberry or Chinese gooseberry, as its various names might suggest). The fruit is a small round berry, about the size of a marble, full of small seeds. It is bright yellow when ripe and very sweet, making it ideal for baking into pies and making jam.

Its most notable feature is the single papery pod, like a Chinese lantern, that covers each berry. Because of the fruit's decorative appearance, it is sometimes used in restaurants as an exotic garnish for desserts.

The Cape gooseberry is native to Brazil, but long ago became naturalised in the highlands of Colombia, Chile and Peru, where the fruits are casually eaten and occasionally sold in markets, but the plant is still not an important crop. It was widely introduced into cultivation in other tropical, subtropical and even temperate areas and grown by early settlers of the Cape of Good Hope before 1807. Soon after its adoption in the Cape of Good Hope (presumably the origin of the name 'Cape gooseberry') it was carried to Australia, where it was one of the few fresh fruits of the early settlers in New South Wales. There it has long been grown on a large scale and is abundantly naturalised, as it is also in Queensland, Victoria, South Australia, western Australia and northern Tasmania.

The Cape gooseberry is now cultivated commercially in the UK, US and Asia. It is also commercially grown in South Africa where canned fruits and jam are staple commodities and often exported. It is also grown on a small scale in Gabon and other parts of Central Africa.

In the UK Cape gooseberries can be grown successfully from seed both indoors and out.

CARISSA BISPINOSA

The genus *Carissa* consists of evergreen shrubs and trees, with handsome, glossy foliage and fragrant, starry-white, jasmine-like flowers. Ornamental and edible, scarlet to crimson oval fruits are produced after flowering. Carissas are attractive, ornamental shrubs and make excellent hedges. In late summer, local inhabitants along the coastal areas of KwaZulu-Natal often sell the fruit to travellers, especially *Carissa macrocarpa*, big num-num

(English), grootnoemnoem (Afrikaans), Amantungulu (Zulu). *Carissa bispinosa*, however, with much smaller leaves, flowers and fruit, does not have to take a back seat as far as the taste of the fruit is concerned!

This species is only occasionally tree-like (up to 5 metres/about 16 feet) and is more often a dense bush or rambling shrub in wooded spots or scrub. Flowers are small, white or tinged pink, with a long, slender corolla tube, sweetly scented and clustered at the tips of twigs. Fruit are small, ovoid, edible red berries. The whole fruit, including the seed, is edible and although the skin is slightly milky, it has a delicious flavour. It is not uncommon to find fruit and flowers on the same plant.

Carissa bispinosa is found in wooded areas from the south-western parts of the Western Cape along the coastal areas right through the Eastern Cape, KwaZulu-Natal into Gauteng and the northern provinces. It also occurs in the Eastern Free State, Lesotho, Swaziland, Zimbabwe and Mozambique, extending westwards to Botswana and Namibia and sporadically further north as far as Kenya. The leaves and thorns, in particular, show marked variation throughout the distribution range.

The name 'Carissa' is derived from the Indian name for plants of this genus, which contain a bitter and poisonous glucoside in the bark called carrisin. The word 'bispinosa' is derived from a Latin word that means two-spined, referring to the forked spines of the plants. The vernacular name num-num could either be of Hottentot origin, or an example of onomatopoeia expressing the sound of pleasure at the taste of the juicy little fruit of this plant.

Traditionally, the plants are not only used for the edible fruit; while the berries are used to make jams and jellies, the indigenous people even used the roots to treat toothache. *Carissa bispinosa* is also used in an annual Swazi ceremony, increasing the courage and ferocity of a black bull before Swazi warriors have to be tested by killing the bull with their bare hands.

CHOKEBERRIES AND CHOKECHERRIES

The chokeberries (*Aronia*) are two species of deciduous shrubs in the rose family, native to eastern North America and most commonly found in wet woods and swamps, but far more popular in eastern Europe, where its juice is believed to help people with heart conditions. It is a popular health drink in Poland and even more popular, I hear, in Russia.

The two species are readily distinguished by their fruit colour, from which the common names derive: red chokeberry and black chokeberry. The fruit is small, with an astringent, bitter flavour: it is eaten by birds (who do not taste astringency and feed on them readily), who then disperse the seeds in their droppings. The name 'chokeberry' comes from the astringency of the fruits, which are inedible when raw.

Juice from these berries is astringent and very tart, but high in vitamin C and antioxidants, with a very dark purple colour. Chokeberry juice is probably best sweetened, in which case it tastes a bit like a cross between blackberry and blueberry, though not as fragrant as the latter, or mixed with other juices. The berries are also used to make wine, jam and soft-drink flavouring.

The chokecherry (*Prunus virginiana*), now called black cherry in Canada, is a different species, but is so similar in properties and applications that I am grouping them together. Chokeberries, genus *Aronia*, are often mistakenly called chokecherries. This naming confusion is easy to understand considering there is a cultivar of the chokecherry *Prunus virginiana* 'Melanocarpa' and a species of chokeberry named *Aronia melanocarpa*.

CLOUDBERRIES

The cloudberry (*Rubus chamaemorus*), also called bakeapple in Newfoundland and Cape Breton Island, is a slow-growing alpine or subarctic species of *Rubus*, producing amber-coloured edible fruit. The botanical name (*chamœmorus*) derives from the Greek *chamai* (dwarf) and *morus* (mulberry). Cloudberry is the name for both the plant and the fruit. Cloudberry should not be confused with salmonberry, although the fruit looks similar.

Cloudberries occur naturally throughout the subarctic regions of the northern hemisphere. In Europe they grow in the Nordic countries, especially in Finland; sometimes in the moorlands of Britain and Ireland, the Baltic states and across northern Russia east to the Pacific Ocean. Small populations are also found further south, as a botanical vestige of the Ice Age. In North America, cloudberries grow wild across most of Canada and Alaska, and in the 48 mainland states of the US in northern Minnesota, New Hampshire, Maine and a small population on Long Island, New York.

They grow in bogs, marshes and wet meadows and require sunny exposures in acidic ground. Cloudberry leaves are food for caterpillars of several Lepidoptera species.

Unlike most Rubus, the cloudberry does not self-pollinate. Wide distribution occurs due to the opening of capsules by birds and animals and the excretion of the indigestible seeds. Further distribution arises through its rhizomes (rootstock), which can develop extensive berry patches.

Despite its modern demand as a delicacy exceeding supply (particularly in Norway), the cloudberry is principally a wild plant. Since the middle of the 1990s, however, the cloudberry has formed part of the 'Northernberries' research project. The Norwegian government, in co-operation with Finnish, Swedish and Scottish counterparts, has vigorously pursued the aim of enabling commercial production of various wild berries (Norway imports 200–300 tons of cloudberries a year from Finland). The cloudberry can be cultivated in Arctic areas where few other crops are possible, for example along the northern coast of Norway.

The ripe fruits are golden-yellow, soft and juicy, and are rich in vitamin C. When eaten fresh, cloudberries have a distinctive tart taste. When overripe, they have a creamy texture and flavour somewhat like yogurt. They are often made into jams, juices, tarts and liqueurs. In Finland, the berries are eaten with 'Leipäjuusto' (a local cheese, the name of which translates to 'bread-cheese') and lots of cream and sugar. In Sweden, cloudberries are also used as an ice cream or waffle topping. In Norway, they are eaten with whipped cream and lots of sugar, or in cakes that often contain marzipan. In Canada, cloudberries are used to flavour a special beer. Canadians also use them for jam, but not on the same scale as Scandinavians. In Alaska the berries are mixed with seal oil, reindeer or caribou fat (which is diced up and made fluffy with the seal oil) and sugar to make 'Eskimo Ice Cream', which doesn't sound particularly tempting to me. In fact, nothing like the 'Eskimo Pies' of my childhood, which were delicious chocolate-covered vanilla ice cream bars.

In Finland, liqueurs such as Lakkalikööri are made of cloudberry. It has a strong taste and is extremely sweet. A Finnish friend once brought me a bottle, but I wasn't at all impressed. Cloudberry is also used as a spice for aquavit.

CROWBERRIES

Apparently berry picking is very addictive. If you've ever eaten a pie made with really fresh berries you will agree. In Alaska, there are almost 50 types of berries, most of which are edible. Berry fruit has been a mainstay of the native Alaskan diet forever. One very popular berry is the crowberry (*Empetrum*).

Crowberries are among the berries that look tasty all the time, but, in fact, never are — at least not straight off the plant. Keep in mind that doesn't necessarily mean they aren't good to eat in pies and jellies.

Crowberries are common in bogs and alpine meadows. They taste very bland raw, but according to the Alaskans, when they are sweetened in a pie, they are incredible! (I guess we'll have to take their word for that.) The crowberry is similar in appearance to a blueberry. The Inuit, for whom these berries are a staple, call them, 'Fruit of the North'. Their flowers, male and female, are purple-crimson and inconspicuous and appear from May to June. The berry season usually begins in July and lasts until the first snow. They are said to be at their best when picked after a good frost. Crowberries are extremely high in vitamin C, approximately twice that of blueberries and almost completely devoid of natural acid.

DEWBERRIES

Dewberries (*Rubus* sect. *Eubatus*) are a group of species closely related to blackberries. They are small brambles with berries reminiscent of the raspberry, but are usually purple to black instead of red.

Dewberries are common throughout most of the northern hemisphere, sometimes thought of as a nuisance weed, but the leaves can be used to make tea and the berries are sweet and edible. They can be eaten raw, or used to make cobblers or jam.

The European dewberry (*Rubus caesius*), grows more upright, like other brambles, but is frequently restricted to coastal communities, especially sand dune systems. It has certainly been spotted in the sand dunes of Wales. Dewberry fruits are a deep, almost black, purple and are coated with a thin layer or 'dew' of waxy droplets — they appear sky-blue (*caesius* is Latin for pale blue). It is less sought after, because its fruits are small and retain a markedly tart taste, even when fully ripe.

Some people recommend cutting the berry on the stem and freezing it, to be used like a cherry in a drink. In the US, the plants do not have upright canes like some other *Rubus* species, but have stems that trail along the ground, putting forth new roots along the length of the stem. The stems are covered with fine spines or stickers. When the berries are ripe, they are tender and difficult to pick in any quantity without squashing them, so some berry pickers tend to eat them as they pick them! Anyone picking these wild berries can expect to have their hands stained purple and to have many scratches from the stickers, but I am told the taste of the sweet berries is worth the trouble. The berry itself looks very much like a blackberry, but you rarely find them with as many drupelets (the individual berries) as you get on blackberry stems. The main difference in the berry is that it's somewhat powdery in appearance, having the same mustiness as you get on a grape or a plum.

GOJI BERRIES

Goji berries (*lycium barbarum*) grow on an evergreen shrub found in temperate and subtropical regions in China, Mongolia and in the Himalayas in Tibet. They belong to the nightshade (*Solonaceae*) family. Goji berries have been used in traditional Chinese medicine for millennia and the bulk of the world production is grown in China, but they have recently benefited from increased popularity in the west because of the plethora of antioxidants and nutrients contained in them (and our obsession with exotic healthy berries).

It is said that the Himalayans were the first natural healers, and that they shared their wisdom with the ancient herbalists of China, Tibet and India. One of their most prized secrets was the fruit of the native goji vine, which had been flourishing in the Himalayan valleys since the beginning of time. Those who came there to learn took the goji home with them and planted it in their own valleys, thus spreading the legend of this 'most marvellous and healthful' fruit.

During the Tang Dynasty (around 800 AD), a well had been dug beside a wall near a famous Buddhist temple covered with goji vines. Over the years, countless berries had fallen into the well. Those who prayed there apparently had the ruddy complexion of good health and even at the age of 80 they had no white hair and had lost no teeth, presumably because they drank the water from the well. From this legend, a poem was crafted:

THE WELL OF YOUTHFUL LIVING
A cool well beside the monk's house,
A clear spring feeds the well and the water
has great powers,
Emerald green leaves grow on the wall,
The deep red berries shine like copper,
The flourishing branch like a walking stick,
The old root in a dog's shape signals good fortune,

The goji nourishes body and spirit,
Drink of the well and enjoy a long life.
Liu Yuxi (772–842 AD).

Goji berries, also called wolfberries, are one of the faddy new 'superfoods'. I first saw them, dried, in a fruit and nut kiosk in Paddington Station. And, because I had read about their health properties, I bought a small quantity. I haven't quite figured out what to do with them, because they don't taste like very much, although I have added them to baked goods as one would do with cranberries or raisins. One word of caution, though: it's not a great idea to add goji berries to dry cereal. Because they are small and hard, It is too easy not to chew them and they can cause discomfort to those who have diverticular problems.

The most outrageous claims have been made for these little red berries. They have been called 'the food of immortality' and 'an anti-ageing miracle'. That said, goji berries have long played an important role in traditional Chinese medicine (TCM), where they are believed to enhance immune system function, improve eyesight (particularly night vision), protect the liver, boost sperm production and improve circulation, among other allegations.

As a food, dried goji berries are traditionally cooked before consumption. In the east, they are often added to rice congee and herbal teas, as well as being used in Chinese tonic soups, with chicken and pork dishes, vegetables and herbs. In the west, they are often eaten as a snack, in the same manner as raisins or other dried fruit, although they are more tart and less sweet with a herbal scent. I think they are better in a mixture of dried fruit than on their own.

HAWTHORN BERRIES
Hawthorn (*Crataegus* species) is a small tree or shrub and a member of the rose family. It was hung over the doorway in the Middle Ages to prevent the entry of evil spirits. Hawthorn berry is a tiny red berry that grows on the hawthorn shrub. The berry has strong antioxidant

properties and has been used as an herbal remedy since ancient times.

HONEYBERRIES

Honeyberry (*Lonicera caerulea*), a very hardy and unique small shrub with sweet and tasty fruit, is a species of honeysuckle indigenous to eastern Siberia, the Russian Far East, and northern Japan, where, from ancient times, the native people have gathered and consumed the fruit in large quantities. While the honeysuckle family consists of over 200 species of vines and shrubs, almost all of them are used solely as decorative plants. The edible and very hardy species, honeyberry, is valued for its delicious elongated blueberry-like fruit, its extremely early ripening (often two weeks before strawberries and a month or more before the earliest blueberries) and for its exceptional hardiness, to −40°F (−40°C) or below.

Honeyberries are sweet enough to enjoy fresh, with tiny edible seeds, and can be used in cooking, making delicious jam.

HUCKLEBERRIES

Huckleberries (*Ericaceae Vaccinium*) are members of the heath family, as are blueberries and cranberries, and are native to North America.

Huckleberries hold a place in archaic English slang. The tiny size of the berries led to their frequent use as a way of referring to something small, often in an affectionate way. The phrase 'a huckleberry over my persimmon' was used to mean 'a bit beyond my abilities'. 'I'll be your huckleberry' (used by the character Doc Holliday in the movie *Tombstone*) is a way of saying that one is just the right person for a given job.

When European settlers arrived in the New World, they found several plants that provided small, dark-coloured sweet berries. The berries reminded them of the English bilberry and similar fruits, and they gave them one of the dialect terms they knew for them, hurtleberry, whose origin is unknown (though some say it has something to do with hurt, from the bruised colour of the berries; a related

British dialect form is whortleberry). Very early on, around about 1670, this was corrupted to huckleberry.

As huckleberries are small, dark and rather insignificant, in the early part of the 19th century, the word became a synonym for something humble or minor, or a tiny amount. Later on it came to mean somebody inconsequential. Mark Twain borrowed some aspects of these ideas to name his famous character, Huckleberry Finn. His idea, as he told an interviewer in 1895, was to establish that he was a boy 'of lower extraction or degree' than Tom Sawyer.

Quite how 'I'm your huckleberry' came out of all that with the sense of the man for the job isn't obvious. It seems that the word came to be given as a mark of affection or comradeship to one's partner or sidekick. There is often an identification of oneself as a willing helper or assistant about it.

The huckleberry most prized for flavour is the blue huckleberry, which grows on the Pacific coast of the north-western US and British Columbia. It is often planted in home gardens and western US cooks are very proud of their fresh huckleberry pies, muffins and desserts. I tasted huckleberry pie once on a trip to Oregon. The people I visited had a cabin on Mount Helen and the berries in the pie had been picked there that day. The pie was just wonderful, oozing with beautiful purple juice.

Thousands of years ago, natural wildfires in what is now the western US created openings in forests, which let in light and gave huckleberries room to grow. Native Americans helped this along by burning their fields from time to time to keep the forest back and to increase their huckleberry crop. Huckleberries provided fresh food in the late summer and autumn and dried berries for the remainder of the year. Native Americans still gather huckleberries every year in the Cascade Mountains; many still using the traditional Indian baskets. They observe the harvest with an annual Huckleberry Festival in the autumn to celebrate the arrival of the huckleberries and to give thanks to Mother Earth for their bounty.

JOSTABERRIES

Most of the berries I have talked about in this book have been around for centuries. The jostaberry (*Ribes x nidigrolaria*) is rather unique in that it is a new berry; a complex cross between a gooseberry and a blackcurrant. The jostaberry was under development for more than 30 years by the late Dr Rudolph Bauer in West Germany.

Jostaberry (pronounced yostaberry) is a totally new berry that combines the best qualities of both parents. The objective in developing the jostaberry was to create a good quality berry with a higher yield than the currant, a thorn-free plant (gooseberry thorns aren't a desirable plant trait) and a plant with immunity to or resistance against various diseases.

Dr Bauer achieved these goals. The jostaberry has a new flavour, bringing out the best traits of a gooseberry with a mild hint of blackcurrant. The gooseberry thorns are gone; immunity or resistance against major diseases is built-in, and the production is higher than either of its parents.

The name of the fruit comes from the German words for blackcurrant and gooseberry. The original fruit was made available to the public in 1977, since then the United States Department of Agriculture in Oregon has developed new varieties.

The shiny black fruit, which is globular or ellipsoid, is edible both raw and cooked. It is described as having a taste between that of a gooseberry and a blackcurrant — the gooseberry flavour being more dominant in the unripe fruit, and the blackcurrant notes developing as the fruit ripens. Like blackcurrants, the fruit freezes well, and like many other members of the *Ribes* genus it is rich in Vitamin C.

Jostaberries are excellent for eating, juicing, freezing and processing.

In the UK, the jostaberry is available to plant in home gardens. Because of their popularity, they may be cultivated soon by commercial fruit growers.

JUJUBES

The jujube tree (*Zyzyphus jujuba*) (pronounced ju-ju-be) originated in China, where it has been cultivated for several thousand years. The fresh, fleshy, dark-red jujube fruit is highly desired by many cultures and is available in Korean, Chinese, Vietnamese and Indian stores. It is also called Chinese date.

The jujube tree can be found in southern Europe, Africa, the Middle East and the Far East. The berry is classed with raisins, dates, figs and can be eaten fresh or dried. The fruit is gummy and sweet; a drupe, varying from round to elongated and from cherry-size to plum-size depending on the cultivar. It has a thin, edible skin surrounding whitish flesh of a sweet, agreeable flavour. The single hard stone contains two seeds. The immature fruit is green in colour, but, as it ripens, it goes through a yellow-green stage with mahogany-coloured spots appearing on the skin as the fruit ripens further. The fully mature fruit is entirely red. Shortly after maturing, the fruit begins to soften and wrinkle. The fruit can be eaten after it becomes wrinkled, but most people prefer it during the interval between the yellow-green stage and the red stage. At this point the flesh is crisp and sweet, reminiscent of an apple, but not as juicy.

Under dry conditions jujubes lose moisture, shrivel and become spongy inside. Unlike most fruits, jujubes will dry on the tree after ripening. Although dried jujubes are not as sweet as true dates, its sugars do concentrate, and the flavour is very similar. Dried fruits require no preservative, and they last 'forever'. Tests in Russia indicate a very high vitamin C content. The fruit has been used medicinally for millennia by many cultures. One of its most popular uses is as a tea for a sore throat.

The jujube's sweet smell is said to make teenagers fall in love, and, as a result, in the Himalaya and Karakoram regions, men take a stem of sweet-smelling jujube flowers with them or put it on their hats to attract the opposite sex.

In America and Canada, jujubes are an old-fashioned

confectionery item in insipid fruit flavours, rather than a fruit. They are a bane to dentists because they are hard and gummy and if they are chewed, rather than sucked, they stick to the teeth, removing fillings. They look like miniature drawing pins without the pin and are the butt of many jokes today.

JUNIPER BERRIES
A juniper berry is the female seed cone produced by the various species of junipers. It is not a true berry, but a cone with unusually fleshy and merged scales, which give it a berry-like appearance. The cones from a handful of species, especially *Juniperus communis*, are used as a spice.

Juniper berries also give gin its distinguishing flavour. But juniper is not only good for making martinis. Its berries were used by the Zuni Indians to assist in childbirth, by British herbalists to treat congestive heart failure and stimulate menstruation and by American 19th-century herbalists to treat congestive heart failure, gonorrhoea and urinary tract infections.

Juniper berries are mostly used in northern European and particularly Scandinavian cuisine to impart a sharp, clear flavour to meat dishes, especially wild birds and game. They also season pork, cabbage and sauerkraut dishes. Traditional recipes for choucroute garni, an Alsatian dish of sauerkraut and meat, universally include juniper berries. These spicy, aromatic berries are also used fresh or dried, crushed or whole, to flavour casseroles, marinades and stuffings. They are a good complement to pork — especially pork pâtés — as well as rabbit, beef and duck. They can also be used in sweet, baked goods, such as fruitcake.

The alcoholic beverage gin was developed in the 17th century in the Netherlands. It was first intended as a medication; juniper berries are a diuretic and were also thought to be an appetite stimulant and a remedy for rheumatism and arthritis. The name 'gin' is derived from either the French genièvre or the Dutch jenever, which both mean 'juniper'. Other juniper-flavoured beverages include the Finnish rye-and-juniper beer known as sahti, which is flavoured with both juniper berries and branches.

Juniper berries have been found in ancient Egyptian tombs, like Tutankhamun's, even from species not known to grow in Egypt. The berries imported into Egypt may have come from Greece; the Greeks record using juniper berries as a medicine long before mentioning their use in food. The Greeks used the berries in many of their Olympics events because of their belief that the berries increased physical stamina in athletes. The Romans used juniper berries as a cheap domestically produced substitute for the expensive black pepper and long pepper imported from India. Juniper berries were also used as an adulterant, as reported in Pliny the Elder's *Natural History*:

Pepper is adulterated with juniper berries, which have the property, to a marvellous degree, of assuming the pungency of pepper.

Pliny also, incorrectly as it happens, asserted that black pepper grew on trees that were 'very similar in appearance to our junipers'.

LINGONBERRIES
The *Vaccinium vitis-idaea* — often called lingonberry or cowberry, and also called foxberry, mountain cranberry, lowbush cranberry and partridgeberry (in Newfoundland and Labrador) — is a small evergreen shrub in the flowering heath plant family *Ericaceae* that bears edible fruit.

It is seldom cultivated, but the fruits are commonly collected in the wild. The native habitat is the circumboreal forests of northern Eurasia and North America, extending from temperate into subarctic climates.

The name 'lingonberry' originates from the Swedish word 'lingon' for the native cowberry. Because the names mountain cranberry and lowbush cranberry perpetuate the longstanding confusion between the cranberry and the lingonberry, some botanists have suggested that these names should be avoided. Many restaurants and nutritionists, however, use and recommend these alternate names to help to increase acceptance and consumption of this delicate and exceptionally nutritious fruit that is unknown in many English-speaking countries.

Lingonberries collected in the wild are a popular fruit in northern, central and eastern Europe, notably in Finland, Norway, Denmark, Sweden, the Baltic Countries, Poland, Slovakia and Karelia (Russia), where they can be picked on both public and private lands in accordance with the European tradition of 'everyman's rights'. Because the berries are quite tart, they are almost always cooked and sweetened before eating in the form of lingonberry jam, compote, juice or syrup. The raw fruits are also frequently simply mashed with sugar, which preserves most of their nutrients and flavour and even enables storing them at room temperature (in closed, but not necessarily sealed, containers). Lingonberries served this way or as compote, often accompany game meats and liver dishes. In Sweden and Norway, reindeer steak is traditionally served with gravy and lingonberry sauce. Lingonberry preserve is commonly eaten with meatballs and potatoes in Sweden. A traditional Finnish dish is sautéed reindeer with mashed potatoes and lingonberries, either cooked or raw with sugar. In Poland, lingonberries are often mixed with pears to create a sauce served with poultry or game. They can also be used to replace redcurrants when creating Cumberland sauce to give it a more sophisticated taste.

Lingonberries are also popular as a wild picked fruit in Newfoundland and Labrador, where they are locally known as partridgeberries. In this region they are also incorporated into jams, syrups and baked goods.

Lingonberries are a staple item in Sweden. The Swedish retailer IKEA often sells lingonberry jam and juice in the store and it is used as a key ingredient in dishes served at IKEA self-serve restaurants.

LOGANBERRIES

The loganberry (*Rubus loganobaccus*) is generally thought to be a cross between a European red raspberry 'Red Antwerp' and a native western US blackberry cultivar 'Texas Early' or 'Aughinburgh'.

It was accidentally created in 1880 or 1881 in Santa Cruz, California, by the American lawyer and horticulturist James Harvey Logan. In the 1880s, berry growers began to cross varieties to obtain better commercial varieties. Logan was dissatisfied with the existing varieties of blackberries and tried to cross two varieties to produce a superior cultivar. While attempting this, he accidentally planted them next to an old variety of red raspberry, all of which fruited and flowered together. One of his seedlings is thought to have been the loganberry, a medium-red berry with good flavour, though tart. Since Logan's time, crosses between the cultivars of raspberry and blackberry have confirmed the loganberry's parentage. Logan's original was introduced to Europe in 1897. Luther Burbank also had some success with similar hybrids at the beginning of the 20th century.

The loganberry proved to be productive and well-adapted to local conditions, but its flavour did not prove popular with customers. Its main use was as a parent for further hybrids. It has been used as a parent in more recent crosses between *Rubus* species, such as tayberry (loganberry x raspberry), boysenberry (loganberry x dewberry), youngberry (Burbank's phenomenal berry x dewberry) and olallieberry (black Logan x youngberry). A less widely-accepted theory suggests that the loganberry originated as a red-fruiting form of the common California blackberry *Rubus ursinus*.

Loganberries may be eaten without preparation as well as being used as an ingredient in jams, pies, crumbles, fruit syrups and country wines. Loganberries, in common with other blackberry/raspberry hybrids, can be used inter-changeably with raspberries or blackberries in most recipes.

A use common to southern Ontario, Canada, and western New York, is loganberry juice. While the loganberry is primarily harvested in the western US, growers there were unaware that a niche market existed for a loganberry-derived drink in the east. According to local lore, the loganberry drink was developed by entrepreneurs in the late 1800s at Crystal Beach, a local summertime resort, and one-time amusement park, in southern Ontario. The drink continued to be served at the amusement park and is still produced there. The most popular commercial version is 'Aunt Rosie's', which is commonly enjoyed in western New York.

LYCHEES

The Lychee (*Litchi chinensisis*) is the sole member of the genus *Litchi* in the soapberry family *Sapindaceae*. It is a tropical fruit tree native to southern China. The fruit is a drupe (a fleshy fruit usually having one single hard stone enclosing a seed). The outside of the lychee is covered by a pinky-red, roughly-textured rind that is inedible but easily removed. The inside consists of a layer of sweet, translucent white flesh, rich in vitamin C, with a texture somewhat similar to that of a grape. (Unfortunately, a peeled lychee looks very much like an eyeball and most Western children can't get past what it looks like to taste it!)

A major early Chinese historical reference to lychees was made in the Tang Dynasty, when it was the favourite fruit of Emperor Li Longji (Xuanzong's) favoured concubine Yang Yuhuan (Yang Guifei). The emperor had the fruit, which was only grown in southern China, delivered by the imperial messenger service's fast horses, whose riders would take shifts day and night in a pony express-like manner, to the capital.

The lychee was first described in the west by Pierre Sonnerat (1748–1814) a naturalist and explorer, on return from his travels to China and south-east Asia. It was then introduced to the Réunion Island in 1764 by Joseph-François Charpentier de Cossigny de Palma, another explorer and engineer. It was later introduced to Madagascar, which has become a major producer.

Lychees are extensively grown in the native region of China, and also elsewhere in south-east Asia, especially in

the north of Thailand, Laos, Cambodia, Vietnam, Bangladesh, Pakistan, India, southern Japan, and more recently in California, Hawaii and Florida, the wetter areas of Eastern Australia and subtropical regions of South Africa; they are also found in the state of Sinaloa in Mexico. Lychees require a warm subtropical to tropical climate that is cool, but also frost-free or with only very slight winter frosts not below $-4\,°C$ ($25\,°F$), and with high summer heat, rainfall and humidity. They are also grown as an ornamental tree as well as for their fruit.
Lychees are commonly sold fresh in Vietnamese, Chinese and Asian markets and, in recent years, also widely in supermarkets worldwide. The red rind turns dark brown when the fruit is refrigerated, but the taste is not affected. Lychees are also sold tinned.

The first lychee was launched into space aboard the Bigelow Aerospace spacecraft Genesis II on 28 June 2007 as part of the private aerospace firm's 'Fly Your Stuff' programme. Guy Pignolet de Pluton, a professor at Université de la Réunion in Sainte-Rose, Réunion, provided the lychee which has been imaged on Bigelow Aerospace's website.

MARIONBERRIES
Marionberries are a distinctly American berry, with worldwide appeal. A native of Marion County, Oregon, where they were developed, they are a cross between the Chehalem and Olallie blackberry. The Marionberry captures the best attributes of both berries and yields an aromatic bouquet and an intense blackberry flavour, for which it has become known. This premium-quality flavour, described by tasters as 'earthy cabernet' and 'sweet with notes of tartness', makes the Marionberry a superb choice for canning, freezing, pies, jams, jellies and ice creams and has earned the Marionberry an outstanding reputation worldwide. Best of all, its vibrant purple colour packs a powerful nutritional punch that catapults Marionberries to the top of the antioxidant charts. A bit of trivia — since Marionberry is a variety of berry, rather than a type, it is usually capitalised.

Unfortunately we cannot have fresh Marionberries yet in

the UK, but they are also available puréed, frozen, dried and tinned, so it might be possible to source them here. So far, I have only been able to find Marionberry jam, but would have to import it from the US, which is prohibitively priced because of its shipping weight.

MIRACLE BERRIES

A truly unusual plant, the miracle berry plant (*Synsepalum dulcificum*) can be an interesting addition to a houseplant collection. A sunny windowsill is all you need to grow this plant that will enthrall your friends. The amazing part is what will happen to you when you chew one of the plant's 2 cm (¾ inch) long, attractive red fruits. Once the fleshy, tasteless pulp coats your tongue, everything you eat for the next few hours or so will taste sweet. Bite into a lemon or a lime and the distinctive flavours of these fruits will be enjoyed, but their sourness will not pucker your mouth. Even a sip of straight vinegar will taste sweet. The basis for this reaction is the presence of miraculin in the fruit of this species. This taste-modifying protein does not actually taste sweet, but apparently it binds to receptors of the taste buds, temporarily changing their function. While the taste-modifying capabilities of the fruits have been known for over a century, miraculin was only isolated in the early 1970s. The exact mechanism of action has yet to be made clear, but is the subject of research, especially for its potential use as an 'artificial sweetener'.

In 2005, *The Guardian* newspaper, in a special report about Japan, featured a new Tokyo café offering dieters delicious, if expensive, low-calorie desserts based on the miracle berry. Justin McCurry wrote . . .

Most people would turn their noses up at the food on offer at the Miracle Fruits café in the city's Ikebukuro district. Not one item has more than 100 calories — a fifth of the average dessert — not even the cakes and ice-cream. They are all unbearably sour, palatable only with help from the miracle fruit. All that calorie-conscious sweet-toothed diners have to do is chew the flesh of a berry, taken from the Synsepalum dulcificum plant, for about two minutes, discard the pip, and tuck in. In an instant, the lemons and limes taste as good as an ordinary sugar-laden dessert.

Native to West Africa, the miracle berry is also known as miracle fruit and sweet berry. It grows as a small shrub with an appearance similar to an azalea. Its fruits develop from small white flowers. Intolerant of freezing weather, the miracle berry cannot be planted outdoors in winter climates, but will happily sit on a sunny windowsill until it can be planted outdoors in the summer. Miracle berries have been widely used across many different countries by millions of people, with no confirmed reports of any adverse or allergic reactions, however, they have not yet been approved for human consumption in the EU by the Food Standards Agency, but it is hoped that this will happen very soon. In the meantime, seedlings are available to plant and freeze-dried berries and granules are available to buy on the internet in the UK with the understanding that consumption is done at your own risk.

MULBERRIES
There are basically three varieties of mulberries — white (*Morus alba*), red (*Morus rubra*) and black (*Morus nigra*).

The white mulberry, originally from China, has been cultivated for centuries for its leaves, which are the main food of the silkworm. The tree is named for its white blossoms, not its exceptionally sweet, sticky fruit, which can be white, lavender or black. The white mulberry now grows in Europe and the US.

The red mulberry is American, growing in moist conditions from Canada to southern Texas. It produces deep-red, almost black flavourful berries.

The black mulberry is native to western Asia and has been grown for its fruit in Europe since Roman times. It produces large tasty berries that often fall from the tree before ripening.

I have a mulberry tree in the courtyard of my home, a former silk mill, which does not flower or fruit. Several years ago I had another, which leaned over my driveway and in the autumn dropped voluminous quantities of mulberries on the ground, staining the ground, our shoes and everywhere we walked purple. I had visions of making huge quantities of mulberry jam, but although the berries were sweet, they didn't taste of anything much. It was a pity, because some varieties are much prized by cooks.

You can spot ripe mulberries in season from a distance because the fruits make such a mess on the ground! Taking children mulberry-gathering is great fun. Everyone holds up a drop cloth, while someone climbs into the trees and showers the drop cloth and children with fruit. Do this on a nice day preceded by sunny weather, because rain washes away the berries' flavour.

Use mulberries immediately after picking. They won't last more than a couple of days in the refrigerator. They will ferment or get mouldy, probably because of their high water content and thin skins. There are many ways to cook mulberries once you've eaten your fill of fresh fruit. Cook them in their own juice until the mixture becomes liquid, and makes a sweet mulberry slurry. Add a little lemon juice and orange rind to offset the sweetness, stir in a thickener (cornflour or arrowroot mixed into a paste with a little water) and you have a pudding. If you have tasty mulberries, you can make mulberry pies and mulberry muffins. You can do anything with mulberries you would do with virtually any other berry, and they dry and freeze well. Lemon or lime juice enhances their flavour, since they don't have the acidity of other fruits.

Pyramus and Thisbe, the first love story ever written, compiled by Ovid from earlier Greek folklore tells how red mulberries got their colour:

Pyramus and Thisbe were neighbours who fell in love when they became adults. Their parents disapproved, but the lovers communicated secretly, through a crack in the wall separating their houses. One night, they eloped, but Thisbe was frightened away from their rendezvous point —a white mulberry tree — by a bloody-mouthed lion that had just finished a meal. She escaped and hid, but lost her cloak, which the lion mauled and bloodied.

Pyramus, seeing the bloody-mouthed lion and the cloak, imagined the worst, and impaled himself on his sword. His blood coloured the mulberries red. When Thisbe found him and realised what had happened, she followed him to death on the same sword. The European mulberry species has been red ever since.

ROWAN

The European Rowan (*Sorbus aucuparia*) is a small tree of the rose family growing in a variety of habitats throughout northern Europe and in the mountains of southern Europe and south-west Asia. Its orange-red berries are a favourite food for many birds and are a traditional wild-collected food in Britain and Scandinavia.

Rowan berries can be made into a slightly bitter jelly, which in Britain is traditionally eaten as an accompaniment to game. It can be made into jams and other preserves, on their own, or with other fruits. The berries have many uses in alcoholic beverages: to flavour liqueurs and cordials, to produce country wine and to flavour ale.

The European rowan has a long tradition in European mythology and folklore. It was thought to be a magical tree and protection against malevolent beings.

The density of the rowan wood makes it very usable for walking sticks and magician's staves. This is why druid staffs, for example, have traditionally been made out of rowan wood, and its branches were often used in dowsing rods and magic wands. Rowan was carried on vessels to avoid storms, kept in houses to guard against lightning, and even planted on graves to keep the deceased from haunting. It was also used as protection from witches.

SAPODILLA (NASEBERRY)

The sapodilla (*Manilkara zapota L.*) is believed to be native to Yucatan and possibly other nearby parts of southern Mexico, as well as northern Belize and north-eastern Guatemala. It was introduced long ago throughout tropical America and the West Indies and the southern part of the Florida mainland.

The fruit is round to egg-shaped, 5–10 cm (2–4 inches) in diameter. The skin is brown and scruffy when ripe. The flesh varies from yellow to shades of brown and sometimes reddish-brown, and may be smooth or of a granular texture. The flavour is sweet and pleasant, ranging from a pear flavour to crunchy brown sugar, sort of like a caramelised pear. Fruits can be seedless, but usually have from 3–12 hard, black, shiny, flattened seeds about 2 cm (¾ inch) long in the centre of the fruit.

Most people find it difficult to tell when a sapodilla is ripe enough to pick. With types that shed much of the 'sand' on maturity, it is relatively easy to observe the slight yellow or peach colour of the ripe skin, but with other types it is necessary to rub the scurf to see if it loosens readily and then scratch the fruit to make sure the skin is not green beneath the scurf. If the skin is brown and the fruit separates from the stem easily, without leaking of the latex, it is fully mature, though still hard and must be kept at room temperature for a few days to soften. It is best to wash off the sandy scurf before putting the fruit aside to ripen. It should be eaten when firm to soft, but not mushy.

In the Bahamas, children bury their 'dillies' in potholes in the limestone to ripen, or the fruits may be wrapped in sweaters or other thick material and put in drawers to hasten softening. Fruits picked when they are immature will shrivel as they soften and will be of inferior quality, sometimes with small pockets of gummy latex.

The very rich, sweet flavour of the sapodilla lends itself to being mixed in milk drinks or sweet desserts such as custard and ice cream. Chicle gum is extracted from the sap of the trunk and is used in some natural chewing gums to this day.

It is sometimes possible to find sapodillas in ethnic markets in the UK.

SASKATOONS

The saskatoon (*Amelanchier alnifolia*) is a woody, fruit-bearing perennial shrub belonging to the rose family and is native to the interior of North America ranging from Alaska, the Yukon and Northwest Territories (close to the Arctic Circle), and south to California, Arizona and New Mexico. It is variously called by the common names serviceberry, saskatoon, juneberry, shadberry, sugar pear and Indian pear.

From the Cree Indian word *misaaskwatoomina* (for saskatoon berry) the Saskatoon has long been a treasured wild fruit and a prairie tradition, having been a plentiful staple fruit from the prairies for years. It is often compared to the blueberry in terms of the berry's size, texture and flavour reminiscent of almonds. The saskatoon is a hardy and tolerant fruit species. It is resistant to low temperatures and drought, and grows in a wide range of soil types. It has the capacity to be productive for many years. As well as having value as a fruit, the saskatoon is also an ornamental shrub with masses of showy flowers that appear in the spring, with brilliant foliage in the autumn.

Interest in cultivating the saskatoon has grown because of strong demand and limited supply. The short, dry growing season and harsh winters, typical of the prairie climate, are not conducive to the commercial production of typical domesticated fruit crops, but somehow they favour the saskatoon.

The saskatoon was important to and widely used by North American natives and later European explorers and settlers. Saskatoon blossoms symbolised spring in the tobacco-planting ceremony of the Blackfoot and the Sun Dance was held in July when the fruit was ripe. The fruit was a staple food. The saskatoon, along with the chokecherry and buffalo berry, were often the only kind of fruit available in any quantity. Many tribes held ceremonies and feasts to celebrate the beginning of the saskatoon harvest.

The fruit was steamed and mashed, made into cakes, and

then dried. Pieces were chipped off as needed and added to soups, stews, or boiled to reconstitute them. Pemmican was a mixture of dried meat and saskatoons with an equal amount of melted fat moulded into cakes. Pemmican would keep for months if stored in a cool, dry place, and it was a winter staple of the Plains Indian tribes.

Several parts of the shrub were used medicinally. The wood has a straight grain, and is hard and strong. It was used for making bows, arrows and other tools.
The fruit of the saskatoon was also popular with European explorers and settlers. The saskatoon was often the only fruit available to early prairie settlers and was an important food source for victims of drought and depression in the 1930s.

David Thompson, born in London and apprenticed to the North American fur trade at an early age, reported in 1810:

On the great Plains there is a shrub bearing a very sweet berry of a dark blue colour, much sought after, great quantities are dried by the Natives; in this state, these berries are as sweet as the best currants, and as much as possible mixed to make pemmican; the wood is hard, weighty and flexible, but not elastic, and wherever it can be procured always forms the Arrow of the Indian, I have dwelt on the above, as it (is) the staple food of all persons, and affords the most nourishment in the least space and weight . . .

David Thompson went on to suggest that this fruit ought to be cultivated in Canada and England.

The saskatoon is capable of tolerating wide ranges of soil pH and texture and is also very cold-hardy. The flower buds have been found to have the potential for extreme resistance to low temperature injury (-50 to -60°C/-58 to -76°F)

The first commercial saskatoon orchards were established in the early 1970s, and a second wave was established in the late 1980s and early 1990s.

Currently, the demand for saskatoons far exceeds supply. The saskatoon industry is in its infancy. It has been predicted that over 4,000 hectares of saskatoons will be planted on the prairies in the next 10 to 15 years.

The berries have a pleasing and unique flavour, and are also high in iron and copper. They are good eaten fresh or in desserts. They were also used in medicines for stomach and liver problems, and the juice was used as a dye. They can be propagated from seed, cuttings or suckers.

Saskatoons are currently available in the UK as a dried fruit snack from some supermarkets.

SEA BUCKTHORN BERRIES

The sea buckthorn (*Hippophae rhamnoides*) gets its name from its tendency to grow near the sea, and from the many spines or thorns present on some buckthorn species. Sea buckthorn grows in various regions of Asia, Europe and North America, and is used for preventing soil erosion due to the extensive root system that develops rapidly.

For culinary use the sea buckthorn berry is mainly used for its juice, which is very rich in vitamin C and contains carotenoids (a variant of carotene). The juice can be extracted from the berries without removing them from the bushes by using a specially designed tool.

Because sea buckthorn berries contain lots of malic acid, they have a sour, sharp taste, so, in the kitchen, these berries are commonly used to make juices mixed with other berries or fruits, and as an addition to puddings and soups.

SLOES

Sloes, the fruit of the blackthorn bush (*Prunus spinosa*), a hardy shrub with superb white blossoms in early spring, are pretty much the last fresh fruit you can pick in Britain before winter sets in. And it is worth waiting at least until the first frosts, because these soften up the berries' skin and temper their wicked sharpness a little.

Sloes are the wild ancestor of modern cultivated plums. They are found throughout Britain in hedges, woods and scrubland. The blackthorn's habitat includes urban parks and scrubland too, so seasonal sloe-picking is not just for country dwellers. There is only really one reason to bother poking about in sloe bushes: sloe gin. You can try eating sloes, but it's not a pleasant experience: if there were a scale for astringency, sloes would be off it. They can be used with other fruits in jams and jellies, where their high pectin content makes them useful for getting a good 'set'. But sloe gin is the best place for a sloe. Dorothy Hartley, author of the magnificently eccentric 1950s classic *Food in England*, says it was the original 'mother's ruin, having long been used by old-fashioned country wives in connubial emergencies'. What these emergencies were, Hartley does not record. Since I read that gin was called 'mother's ruin' in 18th-century England, I wonder if it means that the drunkenness that ensued made the sexual act more acceptable or something else entirely.

SZECHUAN PEPPERCORNS

Not all berries are sweet; or even considered fruit. The Szechuan berry, most commonly called Szechuan pepper (*Zanthoxylum piperitum*) is a perfect example. This spice is a copper-coloured berry found on a thorny ash tree which is native to China. The bitter little seeds are removed when the berries have been dried in the sun. The spice has a unique aroma and flavour that is not as pungent as black pepper, and it has slight lemony overtones that creates in the mouth a kind of tingly numbness. Szechuan peppercorns are one of the five spices in Chinese five-spice powder. Called 'sansho' in Japan, they are used in the spice mixture 'shichimi togarashi', or Japanese seven-spice seasoning.

Szechuan peppercorns are best purchased whole and ground as needed. They can sometimes be found in bulk at health food and gourmet stores.

Recipes often suggest lightly toasting and then crushing the tiny seedpods before adding them to food. Only the husks are used; the seeds are discarded or ignored. It is generally added at the last moment. The hint of pepper and lemon provided by this spice gives a sparkling freshness to young asparagus or an artichoke mousse. It is perfect with sole or salmon, duck or chicken dishes, as well as fried aubergine. And, unexpectedly, it complements a chocolate mousse or a pineapple sorbet.

Star anise and ginger are often used with Szechuan peppercorns, and of course it figures prominently in spicy Szechuan cuisine.

YUMBERRY

Another new to Westerners, the yumberry is now being marketed in the US and Canada and will probably be introduced to Europe soon.

Yum, short for yummy, derived from its native name Yang Mei. It has been harvested in China for over 2,000 years, for its healthy attributes. This deep-red fruit is high in antioxidants and contains a wide range of vitamins, including vitamin C, thiamine, riboflavin and carotene.

Yumberry juice has a sweet/tart balance that can either stand alone or be mixed with other juices or flavours.

Zhejiang Yumberry Juice Co. Ltd. is the world's first manufacturer specialising in producing yumberry healthy products. Currently, its leading products are 10% yumberry juice drink, 100% yumberry juice and yumberry juice concentrate. The concentrate is used in diverse applications ranging from fruit juices to bakery applications, wines, cocktails and dairy products.

Apparently yumberry is one of those rare 'good for you' healthy fruits that actually tastes great on its own or can be blended with other juices to add nutritional value and a unique rich flavour. It is expected that yumberry will grow in popularity much like other high antioxidant fruits, such as acai and pomegranate, have in recent years.

Poisonous
Berries

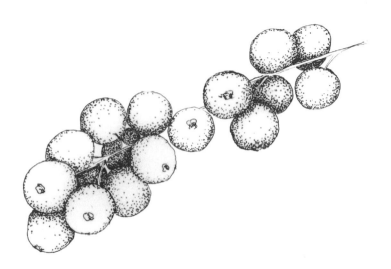

Berry picking can be as dangerous as mushroom picking. It is sometimes hard to resist tasting berries we encounter on nature walks. But they, and many of the beautiful berry-bearing plants we choose for our gardens, could literally be the death of us, since a large variety of plants produce tasty-looking berries that could be fatal.

This is by no means a complete list of poisonous berries, but it's a good start. If you have any of these in your garden, it would be prudent to replace them with something more benign. Adults can be warned, but children and animals are very much at risk.

Castorbean or **Castor Oil** plant (*Ricinus communis*) produces a large fruit-like body that has been responsible for a number of deaths due to its excessively high toxicity. The deeply-grooved, prickly, spherical, fruits are brown in colour and contain three seeds. It is these seeds which contain the most toxin. Produced all year round, they appear in open clusters on a tall spike above the broad-leafed foliage. When ripe, the fruit explosively disperses the seeds.

Deadly Nightshade (*Atropa belladonna*) is also very poisonous. Known as belladonna, this plant produces shiny black berries with a five-lobed calyx on a short stalk. Berries are produced singularly and are about the size of a cherry. They appear in September after the flowers have faded and dropped. The berries have a sweet flavour which appeals particularly to children.

Elderberry (*Sambucus*) makes beautiful wine and jams, but the unripe berries are in fact toxic. The berries are produced in late spring in dense clusters. At the poisonous stage, they are small and pea-like with a short stalk.

English Ivy (*Hedera helix*) has small dark purple berries which appear in clusters. They look similar to blackcurrants in shape, dimension and colour, which children could easily mistake them for. They are produced from late winter through to early spring. Both the leaves and the berries are toxic and can cause oral and stomach irritation, diarrhoea, breathing problems, coma and death. Keep animals, especially curious nibblers, away from English ivy. Exercise caution for indoor animals as well, since English ivy grows up the sides of buildings and can spread through window openings.

Lantana (*Lantana Camara*), also known as Red Sage, can be fatal, affecting the lungs, kidneys, heart and nervous system. It grows in the southern US and in moderate climates. Lantana produces masses of edible, currant-sized bluish-black shiny berries that appear in late summer. They are produced in open clusters on short stems above the foliage. But, like many berries, they are somewhat poisonous when the berries are green and immature. It is strongly suspected that all lantana leaves are toxic if eaten.

Potatoes also produce berries after flowering. These berries contain a very deadly alkaloid poison and have been responsible for a number of fatalities. The berries appear in clusters on a short stalk. Each cluster contains an average of six berries. Small, shiny and green, the berries have a five-lobed calyx and are topped by a short stalk.

Privet (*Ligustrum vulgare*) common in many gardens, privet produces small berries that mature to a dull black colour in winter. They persist for most of the year, hanging in dense grape-like clusters. Privet can cause asthma in some people. Privet berries may be poisonous, especially to small children, and privet flowers can cause hay fever and other allergic reactions.

Rowan berries (*Sorbus aucuparia*) There is much debate as to the toxicity of rowan berries. These are bright orange or red fruit that appear in dense clusters. Some sources say the berries are poisonous while others state the opposite. If we look at the facts, both sources are right. The berries contain parasorbic acid in their raw form. In this state, they are indeed poisonous. On cooking however, the parasorbic acid is converted into harmless sorbic acid, which is edible. Rowan berries are used to make a somewhat bitter jelly that goes well with wild game and is also used in preserves.

Virginia Creeper (*Parthenocissus quinquefolia*) produces berries which are about 6 mm (¼ inch) in diameter. A bluish-black colour, they are produced in open clusters on a central stem and ripen in October. Virginia creeper berries are highly toxic to humans and may be fatal if eaten. Its sap can also cause skin irritation in some people.

Yew (*Taxus baccata*) all parts of the yew are extremely poisonous. The only exception is the fleshy part of its arils (berries), but the seed within is deadly. This is definitely not a tree for self-medication! Yew berries cause a high percentage of poisonings. Most poisonings are due to the bright colouration of the berries and their deceptively appetising appearance, making them attractive to children. The berries are about 8-10mm (⅓ inch) in diameter. Bright scarlet in colour, they have a cup-like depression at the base. The inside of this depression contains the lethal dark-coloured seed.

DEADLY DECORATIONS

Another pair of plants that have caused fatalities, particularly around Christmas time are the berries of both **Holly** (*ilex*) and **Mistletoe** (*viscum album*). Holly produces both yellow and red berries in open clusters of 4–6 berries. The berries are about 8mm in diameter and oval in shape. They ripen from autumn through to early winter. Mistletoe produces translucent white berries that are between 6–10 mm (¼–⅓ inch) in diameter. They are produced in clusters that originate from a central stalk, maturing from January through to March. It pays to keep an eye on children if they are within reach of these decorations, because the berries may be mistaken for just another delicious Christmas treat, with fatal results.

The best way to avoid a poisoning is through education and common sense. Teach your children never to eat any part of a plant either in the wild or in a garden, especially the berries, no matter how delicious it looks, without asking for permission. Try to teach yourself and your children to recognise edible fruits, berries and vegetables. If you cannot identify what it is, they should be forbidden to experiment. The same advice also applies to adults. Never taste unidentified berries. Just because some berries are safe for birds and animals to eat does not mean they will not have a lethal reaction on humans. This mistake has cost lives in the past. Never leave small children on their own in a garden containing suspect or hazardous plants. Children have a natural curiosity and if it appears good enough to eat, they will try it. Better still, don't take any chances. Replace any poisonous plants in your garden. No plant is beautiful enough to risk the lives of children or pets.

If you suspect someone has eaten poisonous berries, seek medical attention immediately. Take a sample of the berries with you, as this will aid the medical staff in identifying the toxin and treating the patient.

Picking Your Own

If you love berries and other fruits and vegetables, you might want to pick your own.

The quality is much better than any shop or farmers' market, when you choose the fruit and get it right from the plant. It looks and tastes better. The produce is healthier, too, because it is fresher and you can choose farms with organic produce. The costs are usually substantially less than buying from a shop or market; the farmer doesn't need to pay labour to pick, and he or she has no packaging or shipping costs. If you plan to can or preserve any jam, fruit or vegetables, this is the best way to get the quantity, quality and price you want. And, finally, it's fun: families and couples like to do it to get outside, participate in something active and spend time together. Kids love it!

A very good website for PYO farms all over the world is: www.pickyourown.org

The UK link is:
www.pickyourown.org/unitedkingdom.htm

Just click on a link to find an area and farm near you. Be SURE to call before you go. Crops don't ripen according to a precise schedule, so if they are not ripe, the farm won't be open. And some of these farmers are not the world's best business people, so they may keep erratic hours or close unexpectedly, or just not answer their phone. Once you've found a farm and have established that it is open, here are some tips the site offers:

It is a good idea to pack for a day trip — bring snacks, disposable wipes and plenty of liquids to drink.

Bring containers for picking (smaller containers are better for children's smaller hands).

Dress in old clothes and old trainers; you want to be comfortable and not worried about staining or tearing your clothes! If the ground is wet, it will really ruin any nice shoes, so wear your old ones!

Don't forget sunscreen for any exposed areas of skin (face, back of neck, arms, legs).

Wide-brimmed hats help to protect you from the summer sun; and, in the autumn, extra layers keep you warm.

The weather could change without notice. If you get hit by a downpour, be ready to switch to plan B, such as a visit to a museum, tourist or historic site nearby.

Pack a picnic lunch and snacks. You'll be gone all day and all that picking and being outdoors will work up a big appetite (assuming the children haven't already gorged on the fruit they're picking). Bring a cool bag and pack it with your favourite lunch and snacks. Eating outdoors is part of the experience! However, if you don't want to drag a lot of stuff around and the farm has a teashop or café, that could be another possibility.

Don't forget your camera. You may want to capture those memories you're making. But remember you'll be on a farm, so bring a cheap or disposable camera, rather than the expensive one.

When you arrive at the farm, take some time at the beginning to explain to your children how to identify and pick ripe fruit. If you don't know, read the website's tips for the fruit you want to pick, or ask the farmhands. And since fields and orchards can be large, make sure everyone knows where to meet up should you get separated!

The fun doesn't have to end with just picking the fruit. Some farms also offer hay rides, petting zoos, corn mazes, gift shops, even restaurants. And if your children tire before you've had your fill of fruit, most places also sell pre-picked produce. Even if you don't actually pick it yourself, you'll still get better quality and a better price than at the supermarket.

Very Berry
Good for You

HEALTH BENEFITS OF BERRIES

We are constantly being admonished to eat five helpings of fruit and vegetables a day. Some cancer specialists say to include berries three to four times a week. This is good news because berries aren't only beautiful and delicious, they are very berry good for you — many of them pack powerful health benefits. Berries contain an abundance of plant chemicals called phytochemicals, which are micronutrients that help our bodies fight disease.

Phytochemicals are found in plants; for example, fruits, vegetables, grains, pulses, seeds and roots. Scientists now rank berries as having the highest levels of anthocyanins, one of the most important groups of phytochemicals. These water-soluble plant pigments are responsible for the colour of berries — they make blueberries blue and raspberries and cherries red, and they will stain your clothing if you are not careful.

Although approximately 90% of berries are juice, this juice is packed with powerful antioxidants and other disease-fighting components, providing berries with an important role in maintaining good health.

We are told that the darker coloured the berry, the greater the anthocyanin level; consequently the more health-giving it is. Everyone in the food and vitamin supplement sector seems to feel that 'their' berry is the new 'superfood'— the ultimate panacea. The important point to remember is that there is no miracle ingredient that will prevent and cure all ills. We can only try to maintain a healthy diet by eating a variety of foods, with an emphasis on fruits, vegetables and grains.

Anthocyanins are like an antivirus package for our bodies — helping to prevent disease before it starts. Anthocyanins have been linked to antiviral and anticancer activity, controlling diabetes, reducing coronary heart disease, retarding the effects of ageing and improving vision.

Berries also contain significant amounts of phenolic acid, another vital phytochemical, which interacts with the anthocyanins, stimulating the enzymes in our body to detoxify, which helps to protect the digestive system from developing cancers of the oesophagus and colon.

Tannins, another member of the phenolic family, with high concentrations in cranberries and other berries, help to prevent urinary tract infections.

Clearly, it is the combination of all the phytochemicals and nutrients in fresh berries (anthocyanins, phenolic acid, fibre, tannin, vitamins and minerals) that work together to help to prevent disease. But what about cooked and dried berries? Nutraceutical levels in some berries are not affected by heat processing, but may be diminished in others. Obviously the benefits will not be as great as eating raw berries, but it's better than not eating any.

Some of the berries that have particular value in terms of health are listed below with their claims, some of which are unsubstantiated. It is unlikely that they will do you any harm (unless of course you are allergic to them), but on the other hand, they are only part of the recipe for good health.

ACAI BERRIES
This little berry is touted as being one of the most nutritious and powerful foods in the world! Acai (ah-sigh-ee) is the high-energy berry of a special Amazon palm tree. Harvested in the rainforests of Brazil, acai tastes like a vibrant blend of berries and chocolate. Hidden within its royal purple pigment is the magic that makes it nature's perfect energy fruit. Acai is packed full of antioxidants, amino acids and essential fatty acids. Although acai may not be available in your local supermarket, you can find it in several health food and gourmet stores (often in juice form). A new product featuring the unsweetened pulp is now also available.

Acai pulp contains a remarkable concentration of antioxidants that help to combat premature ageing, with

10 times more antioxidants than red grapes and 10–30 times the anthocyanins of red wine. It offers a synergy of monounsaturated fats, dietary fibre and phytosterols to help to promote cardiovascular and digestive health. It is an almost perfect essential amino acid complex in conjunction with valuable trace minerals, vital to proper muscle contraction and regeneration.

The fatty acid content in acai resembles that of olive oil, and is rich in monounsaturated oleic acid. Oleic acid is important for a number of reasons. It helps omega-3 fish oils to penetrate the cell membrane; together they help make cell membranes more supple, which makes all hormones, neurotransmitter and insulin receptors function more efficiently. This is particularly important because high insulin levels create an inflammatory condition and inflammation causes ageing.

ALLSPICE

Because of its eugenol content, allspice has attributes similar to clove. It is a digestive and carminative (an agent that induces the expulsion of gas from the stomach or intestines). The oil is classed as rubefacient, meaning that it irritates the skin and expands the blood vessels, increasing the flow of blood to make the skin feel warmer. The tannins in allspice provide a mild anaesthetic that, with its warming effect, make it a popular home remedy for arthritis and sore muscles, used either as a poultice or in hot baths.

ARONIA (CHOKEBERRIES)

Aronia berries are said to have the highest levels of natural antioxidants of any fruit.

More than even blueberries and the often bragged about pomegranate, aronia berries boast the richest fruit source of anthocyanins and other antioxidants. Several studies have shown aronia to help in the treatment of diabetes, urinary tract infections, cancer, cardiovascular ailments and influenza.

Aronia has an ORAC (oxygen radical absorptive capacity – measure of an antioxidant's power to neutralise free radicals) value higher than any other food. This is due to the high concentration of anthocyanins and proantho-cyanidinsm (a class of flavonoids), both of which contribute to aronia's dark, almost black colour.

BEARBERRIES

Perhaps this is cheating a little because it is the leaf, rather than the berry, that is beneficial. Smoking the leaves of bearberries as a tobacco substitute is the most widely mentioned human use of bearberry.

Medical uses of bearberry leaves were recognised by early Romans, Native Americans and settlers. Bearberry leaves are used still used medicinally in Poland and other countries. The most important medical use of the leaves is for treating urinary tract disease. They can also be used to make a highly astringent wash and as a vasoconstrictor for the endometrium (mucus membrane) of the uterus.

BILBERRIES

Often associated with improvement of night vision, bilberries, a close relative of blueberries, are mentioned in a popular story of World War II RAF pilots consuming bilberry jam to sharpen vision for night missions. However, a recent study by the US Navy found no such effect, and origins of the RAF story cannot be found.

Laboratory studies have shown that bilberry consumption can inhibit or reverse eye disorders such as macular degeneration, but this therapeutic use remains clinically unproven.

As a deep-blue fruit, bilberries contain dense levels of anthocyanin pigments that have been linked experimentally to lowered risk for several diseases, such as those of the heart and cardiovascular system, eyes and cancer.

In folk medicine, bilberry leaves were used to treat gastrointestinal ailments, applied topically or made into infusions. Such effects have not been proved scientifically.

Bilberry fruit and its extracts contain a number of

biologically active components, including a class of compounds called anthocyanosides (which literally means 'blue colouring substance of flowers'). These have been the focus of recent research in Europe.

Bilberry extract has been evaluated for efficacy as an antioxidant, mucostimulant (stimulating the mucous membranes), hypoglycaemic (lowering the glucose content in the blood), anti-inflammatory, blood vessel protector and lipid (fat)-lowering agent. Although pre-clinical studies have been promising, human data is limited and largely of poor quality. At this time, there is not sufficient evidence in support of (or against) the use of bilberry for most indications. Notably, the evidence does not endorse using bilberries for the improvement of night vision.

CLOUDBERRIES
Due to its high vitamin C content, the cloudberry is valued both by Nordic seafarers and by Canadian Inuit as a protection against scurvy. Its high benzoic acid content acts as a natural preservative.

Tea made from cloudberry leaves was used in ancient Scandinavian herbal medicine to cure urinary tract infections.

ELDERBERRIES
According to the plethora of literature concerning this member of the honeysuckle family, elderberries contribute much to wellbeing.

Elderberries were called the 'medicine chest of the common people' by Native Americans. The therapeutic benefits of the elder plant include it being used as an astringent, immunostimulant, emetic, expectorant, diaphoretic, laxative, diuretic, sedative and anti-inflammatory. Elder is also said to be an excellent blood cleanser (it helps to eliminate waste in the fluid surrounding the blood cells).

It has been a traditional remedy for fever, colds, influenza and respiratory infections. In addition, elderberries can be used to treat chronic rheumatism, neuralgia and sciatica.

Elder is also an effective detoxifier and can be used topically to clear infections such as acne, boils and skin rashes.

Elderflowers contain three rich sources of potassium plus viburnic acid (helpful for asthma and bronchitis), volatile oils, vitamin A, vitamin C and bioflavonoids. Elderberry jam/jelly contains many vitamins and minerals. In fact, elderberries contain more vitamin C than any other herb except for blackcurrants and rosehips!

Research indicates that elderberries stimulate and build up the resistance of the immune system, and directly inhibits the influenza virus. Elderberries have an enzyme that smoothes down the pointed spikes on the outside of the virus, which it uses to pierce through the cell walls.

A few clinical studies of Sambucol®, a formulation based on an extract of elderberry, have shown that it might be effective in the treatment of both adults and children with either type A or B influenza. Sambucol® reduced both the severity and duration of influenza symptoms in otherwise healthy subjects, but should not be considered a substitute for influenza vaccination in high-risk individuals. An *in vitro* study of Sambucol® showed possible effectiveness against the H5N1 strain of bird flu.

HAWTHORN BERRIES
By the early 1800s, doctors recognised the herb's medicinal properties and began using it to treat circulatory disorders and respiratory illnesses. Considered a 'cardiotonic' herb or heart tonic, the flowers and berries of the hawthorn plant were used in traditional medicine to treat irregular heartbeat (arrhythmia), normalising blood pressure (not only lowering it when it is high, but raising it when it is low), hardening of the arteries and heart failure. Compounds in hawthorn can help to protect the heart against oxygen deprivation, a condition that often leads to angina, a disease marked by intense chest pain.

Today, hawthorn berries are one of the most valuable medicinal herbs used in the treatment of congestive heart failure and circulatory disorders.

Hawthorn is rich in bioflavonoids, which relax and dilate the arteries. These compounds are powerful antioxidants that help to increase the flow of blood and oxygen to the heart. This reduces the work required by the heart to circulate blood, and in turn reduces blood pressure and stress to the heart muscle. The bioflavonoid substances give strength to the walls of blood vessels and improve blood flow to other areas of the body. Components in hawthorn have been shown to lower cholesterol and the amount of plaque in arteries.

Hawthorn is a diuretic, helping to rid the body of excess salt and water, supporting weight loss programmes. It has also been used to treat digestive problems, nervous tension, insomnia and sore throats. Combined with ginkgo biloba, it works to enhance poor memory by improving circulation of blood within the head and increasing the amount of oxygen to the brain.

A hawthorn extract was recently found to be effective for hypertension in patients with type 2 diabetes who were also taking their prescribed medicines. Patients took 1,200 mg hawthorn extract daily or a placebo for 16 weeks. Those taking the hawthorn supplement had lower blood pressure than those taking the placebo.

Hawthorn is best used long term, because the active constituents do not produce rapid results. The benefits develop slowly, and have a direct effect on the heart, especially in cases of heart damage and heart problems associated with liver disease. It is thought to be gentle and safe for long-term use with no toxic side effects.

Hawthorn berry supplements are available in capsules and tinctures. Teas can also be made from dried hawthorn leaves, flowers and berries.

What about hawthorn berry side effects? Hawthorne berry is considered to be among the safest herbal supplements. Some rare side effects may include nausea, rapid heartbeat or headache. There are some drug interactions possible with hawthorn berry, so people using it should consult a physician if they are taking any prescription medications. For example, it may enhance the activity of the heart medication Digoxin. It can also counteract the effects of products, such as nasal decongestants, that contain phenylephrine. Phenylephrine constricts blood vessels, so the ability of hawthorn berry to dilate blood vessels will decrease the effectiveness of medications that contain it.

JUJUBE

The Chinese discovered jujube over 4,000 years ago. Over the centuries they have established great herbal remedies utilising all parts of the jujube tree, particularly the dried fruit, which is said to improve liver problems and to rehydrate the body and soothe the vital organs. They believe the jujube can cure coughs and sore throats, eliminate influenza symptoms and solve breathing problems. The continuous usage of jujube, according to the Chinese, will improve skin colour and cure skin infections. Lastly, the Chinese believe that the jujube fruit will kill internal parasites and worms. Very few plants or trees are revered and loved by the Chinese as the jujube tree, for its natural medical remedies.

Jujube contains fruit acids, sugars, hydroxycoumarins, triterpenes, peptide alkaloids, isoquinoline alkaloids, flavonoids, tannins, mucilage and triterpene saponins. Jujube is emollient and has demonstrated anti-allergenic, sedative and hypotensive effects. Jujube has been used for improving muscle strength, a lack of appetite, rehydrating dry and irritated skin, fatigue, diarrhoea, wounds, inflammation, ulcers and fever. In addition, jujube has been used in topical formulations as an anti-inflammatory, anti-wrinkle preparation, moisturiser and sunburn soother.

Modern medical research is looking into the efficacy of jujube for the treatment of cancer and HIV, and the cosmetic industry is very excited about jujube's ability to slow down the ageing process.

JUNIPER BERRIES

Juniper berries have been used as a fragrance since ancient times, and were thought to purify the air where they were used. Juniper has a pleasing floral aroma that is uplifting and stimulating. It was once considered to have the power to restore lost youth. Juniper was one of the first aromatics used in ancient civilization, and has a colourful history of use. The ancient Greeks burned juniper branches to combat epidemics. The English burned it as well, and hoped its magical powers would repel evil spirits, witches and demons. Ancient Egyptians anointed corpses with juniper oil, and used the berries in cosmetics and perfumes. Europeans regarded juniper oil as a miracle cure for typhoid, cholera, dysentery and tapeworms. Many cultures today still value juniper's many benefits. Tibetans still revere juniper and use it as a purification incense, while Native Americans burn it in their cleansing ceremonies. Holistic medicine also embraces juniper.

Contemporary herbalists primarily use juniper as a component of herbal formulas designed to treat bladder infections. A typical combination might include bearberry, parsley, red clover and the herb buchu. Such formulas are said to be most effective when taken at the first sign of symptoms, but they might not work well once the infection has really taken hold. Unfortunately, double-blind studies of juniper have not been performed.

Recently, gin-soaked raisins have been touted as an arthritis treatment. This is probably just a fad, but some weak evidence suggests that juniper may possess anti-inflammatory properties. In the test tube, juniper has also been shown to inhibit the herpes virus.

You can make juniper tea by adding 240 ml (8 fl oz) boiling water to 1 tablespoon juniper berries, covering, and allowing the berries to steep for 20 minutes. The usual dosage is 1 cup twice a day. However, juniper is said to work better as a treatment for bladder infections when combined with other herbs. Combination products should be taken according to label instructions.

Warning: Bladder infections can go on to become kidney infections. For this reason, seek medical supervision if your symptoms don't resolve themselves in a few days, or if you develop intense lower back pain, fever, chills or other signs of serious infection.

Although juniper is regarded as safe, and is widely used in foods, we don't recommend taking it during pregnancy. (We also recommend not drinking gin.) Remember, juniper was used historically to stimulate menstruation and childbirth. It has also been shown to cause miscarriages in rats.

Juniper seldom causes any noticeable side effects. Prolonged use of juniper could possibly deplete the body of potassium, the way other diuretics do, but this hasn't been proven. Combining juniper with conventional diuretics, however, may cause excessive fluid loss.

LINGONBERRIES

Lingonberries contain plentiful organic acids, vitamin C, provitamin A (as beta carotene), B vitamins (B1, B2, B3), and the elements potassium, calcium, magnesium and phosphorus. In addition to these healthful nutrients, lingonberries also contain phytochemicals that are thought to counteract urinary tract infections, and the seeds are rich in omega-3 fatty acids.

Lingonberries were a major component in keeping people healthy in Sweden through the long winters without fresh vegetables. A coarse porridge with fat salt pork and lingonberry preserve was a classic meal of the winter, and a large crock of the berries preserved with sugar would be found in every larder. Owing to their high content of benzoic acid, lingonberries have the additional virtue of being able to be made into preserves without boiling.

MULBERRIES

In traditional European medicine, the mulberry root is a remedy for tapeworms. The tree's inner bark (cambium) has been used as a laxative. The fruit, eaten in very large quantity, may also be mildly laxative.

PARTRIDGE BERRIES

Partridge berries (*Mitchella repens*), also called squaw berries, are a uterine relaxant reputed to promote an easy labour by aiding contraction of the womb during childbirth. Native American women used this herb in the last weeks of pregnancy to prepare themselves for childbirth.

It is also recommended for dysmenorrhoea and other painful conditions of the female reproductive tract. It has a calming effect on the nervous system and, in addition, improves the digestion. As an astringent, it has been used in the treatment of colitis, especially if there is much mucus. It may be used in nervous exhaustion, irritability or debility in either sex, especially when symptoms involve the reproductive system. There are no culinary applications.

ROWAN BERRIES

In folklore, fresh rowan berry juice has been used as a laxative, gargle for sore throats, medicine for inflamed tonsils and hoarseness, and as a source of vitamins A and C. Rowan berry jam will supposedly remedy diarrhoea. An infusion of the berries will benefit haemorrhoids and painful urination. The bark can also be used as an astringent for loose bowels and vaginal irritations. In addition, rowan is used for eye irritations, spastic pains in the uterus, heart/bladder problems, neuralgia and gout.

SEA BUCKTHORN BERRIES

Different parts of sea buckthorn have been used as traditional therapies for diseases. The bark and leaves are used for treating diarrhoea, gastrointestinal and dermatologic disorders and topical compressions for rheumatoid arthritis. Flowers may be used as a skin softener. For its haemostatic and anti-inflammatory effects, sea buckthorn berry fruits are added to medications for pulmonary, gastrointestinal, cardiac, blood and metabolic disorders in Indian, Chinese and Tibetan medicines. And research has shown that sea buckthorn berry components may also have potential anti-carcinogenic activity.

SCHIZANDRA BERRY (*Schisandra chinensis*)
Used worldwide as an astringent tonic to strengthen the cell tissues and to retain body energy, Schizandra is currently very popular. As an adaptogen (compounds which regulate bodily functions) this herb increases the energy supply of cells in the brain, liver, nerves, muscles, glands and kidneys.

Schizandra is included in liver tonic preparations as it is believed it can improve the bodies' digestion of fatty foods through its ability to cleanse the liver and increase the production of bile, which then functions as a digestive for cleaving the fat into fatty acids and glycerine.

SLOES
Sloe berries are very tonic bitters. They are astringent, stimulate the metabolism, clean the blood and are used as a laxative and diuretic. They help with indigestion, eczema, herpes, allergies, colds, catarrh, neurosis, weak heart, kidney stones, skin, bladder and prostrate problems. They also disperse toxins. In the 17th and 18th century, sloes were brewed as a purgative to treat 'fluxes in the belly'.

I think it is a mistake to self-medicate by picking berries off the trees. Safer remedies for many of the maladies discussed in this section can be purchased from reliable herbalists and health food shops.

Cosmetics and Toiletries

ANTIOXIDANTS AND ANTI-AGEING INGREDIENTS

Ingredients from plant sources are being used more and more in the mainstream cosmetics and toiletries industry in lieu of, and in addition to, chemical components because they are perceived as being more beneficial to the skin.

There are many cosmetics manufacturers who are working in this area and a lot of scientific words being bandied about in the media, but the company mentioned below has just announced a major product launch utilising berries, which will undoubtedly filter down to become components in toiletries and cosmetics all over the world.

Symrise in Holzminden, Germany, is one of the world's leading producers of fragrances, flavours and the raw materials and active ingredients used in cosmetics and toiletries. As such, the company has been working for years to supply the international cosmetics industry with a large array of innovative natural ingredients of proven efficacy. The company now combines its high-quality plant extracts under a new product group: Symrise Actipone®.

Symrise has built its portfolio of extracts to include a number of berries, some of which were not well known in the personal care industry. The company expanded its portfolio of berry extracts to answer the industry's need for antioxidant-rich, anti-ageing ingredients. The new berry extracts, according to the company, contain antioxidants such as anthocyanins and proanthocyanidins. The following is a list of some the berries that Symrise has introduced as part of its antioxidant berry portfolio. This is an example of continuing research into new uses for berry components mentioned in the introduction of this book.

1. **Aronia** (*Aronia melanocarpa* [chokeberry] fruit extract) — Aronia is said to have a high antioxidant content. It is a shrub found in the wet woods of eastern North America. It has been used by Native Americans for nutrition and medicine and was cultivated in Russia at the beginning of the 20th century. It is recommended as a moisturiser for the face, hands and décolletage to help to diminish the signs of wrinkles.

2. **Bilberry** (*Vaccinium myrtillus* fruit/leaf extract) — Bilberry contains high levels of antioxidants, such as vitamin C and anthocyanosides. It also contains tannins, which can be an astringent or an anti-inflammatory. Bilberry is a shrub that is found in northern Europe, Asia and the US Rockies. It is a relative of the blueberry and has been used medicinally for centuries. It is recommended for formulation into cleansers, toners and moisturisers.

3. **Elderberry** (*Sambucus nigra* fruit extract) — Elderberries contain anthocyanins and are thought to improve the immune system. They grow in Europe, the US, central and South America and Australia. Although Egyptians used the berries to heal burns, the British have used them to fight colds. Symrise recommends the elderberry for formulation into an after sun moisturiser.

4. **Blackberry** (*Rubus fructicosus* fruit extract) — Blackberry contains anthocyanosides, vitamins C and E and selenium. They are said to be an anti-inflammatory and they grow in North America and western Europe. The blackberry can be traced back nearly 2,500 years and is recommended for formulation into bath products, body lotions and lip products.

5. **Blackcurrant** (*Ribes nigrum* fruit extract) — Blackcurrant contains a higher concentration of vitamins and minerals than any other fruit, according to Symrise, including potassium, magnesium, iron, calcium, and vitamins A, B and C. The plant is native to central and northern Europe and northern Asia. It was used in the Middle Ages as a herbal medicine and is a popular flavouring in the UK.

It is recommended for formulation into shower gel, body scrub, body cream and hand and foot treatments.

6. **Cranberry** (*Vaccinium oxycoccus* fruit extract) — Cranberries contain high levels of anthocyanidins and vitamin C. The shrubs grow in the northern US and Canada. It was used by the Native Americans as a healing agent and stimulant; it is recommended for stimulant personal care, such as invigorating shower gel and moisturiser.

Berry Recipes

INDEX OF RECIPES

For the most part I prefer to use fresh berries for cold and uncooked dishes and fruit pies and dried berries for other baked goods (such as cakes and cookies) and most cooked foods, because fresh berries in cakes often makes the end result too wet. The heat of the oven plumps up the dried berries nicely. Just to contradict myself, frozen unthawed blueberries and raspberries work wonderfully well in cakes and muffins.

ACAI BERRIES

RASPBERRIES AND ACAI BERRIES IN SYRUP WITH GINGER ICE CREAM

Acai berries, sometimes called palm fruit, are small berries from a species of palm tree. The fruit is used throughout south-east Asia as a sweet element in dessert dishes. Acai berries are small, oblong berries about the size of a small raspberry. The fruit has a gelatine-like texture and a sweet, fragrant aroma that smells like roses. Here we are using them tinned and paired with fresh raspberries to create a delectable dessert.

You will need: **Serves 4**
    225 g (8 oz) fresh raspberries
    170 g (6 oz) acai berries (palm fruit) in red syrup*
    1/8 teaspoon Chinese five-spice powder
    2 tablespoons water
    Bought stem ginger ice cream
    Thin, round, honey-sesame cookies for garnish*
    Mint sprigs for garnish

1. Combine the raspberries, acai berries and their syrup, five-spice powder and water in a small saucepan over a medium-low heat. Heat the mixture just until the syrup simmers and begins to thicken. Do not allow the mixture to boil. Boiling will break down the raspberries. Keep warm until ready to serve.

2. To serve, place a scoop of the stem ginger ice cream in a serving bowl or large martini glass. Spoon some of

the warm raspberry-acai fruit mixture over the ice cream. Place a cookie at an angle in the ice cream and garnish with a sprig of fresh mint.

*Tinned acai berries (palm fruit) is available in 340 g (12 oz) jars and can be found in Asian grocery stores. Any cookies found at the Asian grocery store will do, but I like very thin, round, honey-sesame cookies because they are delicate and crispy.

ALLSPICE

The warm sweet flavour of allspice lends itself to a wide variety of foods, both savoury and sweet.

❐ Try mixing 1/4 teaspoon ground allspice with 900 g (2 lb) minced beef to give a unique taste to meatloaf or hamburgers.

❐ Add 1 teaspoon ground allspice to angel food or pound cake for a sensational spicy flavour.

❐ Aromatic whole allspice is a great addition to potpourri.

❐ Add a few whole allspice berries to your pepper grinder, along with a mixture of black, white and green peppercorns for a unique seasoning blend.

❐ For an intriguing spiciness, add whole, cracked berries to marinades for chicken and pork, simmering beef stew, pot roasts or hearty bean soups.

❐ Enhance simple desserts such as applesauce, fruit compotes and oatmeal cookies with the warm, sweet flavour of ground allspice.

❐ Add a pinch of ground allspice to barbecue and tomato sauces as well as cooked winter squash and carrots.

❐ Allspice may be substituted for cloves.

❐ To grind allspice at home, do not use a grinder with plastic parts, because the oil in the spice can cloud plastic.

JAMAICAN JERK CHICKEN

The jerk seasoning can be made a day in advance. The chicken needs to marinate for at least four hours and can sit as long as overnight.

You will need: **Makes 8 servings**

3 tablespoons dark rum
2 tablespoons water

120 ml (4 fl oz) malt vinegar
10 spring onions, chopped
4 garlic cloves, peeled and chopped
2 tablespoons dried thyme
2 Scotch bonnet chillies or habanero chillies with seeds, chopped
2 tablespoons vegetable oil
4 teaspoons freshly ground allspice
4 teaspoons ground ginger
4 teaspoons ground cinnamon
2 teaspoons ground nutmeg
2 teaspoons salt
2 teaspoons freshly -ground black pepper
2 teaspoons dark-brown sugar
240 ml (8 fl oz) tomato ketchup
3 tablespoons soy sauce

Two 1.35 kg–1.8 kg (3–4 lb chickens, cut into 4 pieces each, rinsed and patted dry
120 ml (4 fl oz) freshly-squeezed lime juice

Salt and freshly-ground pepper to taste

1. Boil the rum and water in a small saucepan for 3 minutes.

2. Transfer the rum mixture to a blender; add the vinegar and the next 12 ingredients and blend until almost smooth. Transfer 2 tablespoons jerk seasoning to a small bowl; mix with the ketchup and soy sauce to make the jerk sauce. (Jerk seasoning and sauce can be made one day ahead; cover separately and refrigerate.)

3. Arrange the chicken in a large roasting tin or baking dish. Pour the lime juice over; turn to coat. Spoon jerk seasoning over the chicken and rub in. Cover and refrigerate for at least 4 hours, turning occasionally. Can be prepared one day ahead. Keep refrigerated.

4. Preheat the oven to 180°C (350°F/Gas Mark 4) or prepare barbecue grill (medium heat). Remove the chicken from jerk seasoning marinade; sprinkle with salt and pepper. If roasting chicken in oven, arrange the chicken, skin side up, on a rimmed baking tray. Roast until the chicken is cooked through and juices run clear when thickest part of thigh is pierced with fork, about 50 minutes. If grilling the chicken, place the chicken, skin side down, on grill rack, cover, and grill until the chicken is cooked through, turning occasionally and adjusting heat if browning too quickly, about 50 minutes.

5. Serve with reserved sauce.

BLACKBERRIES

ASIAN NOODLE SALAD WITH FRESH BERRIES

Dressing: Serves 4

    2 garlic cloves, finely chopped
    1 tablespoon finely chopped fresh ginger root
    4 tablespoons low-sodium soy sauce
    3 tablespoons rice vinegar or white vinegar
    4 tablespoons peanut oil
    3 tablespoons sesame oil
    Dash of hot pepper sauce

    200 g (7 oz) packet Udon noodles
    ½ green pepper, cut into strips
    ½ yellow pepper, cut into strips
    ½ red pepper, cut into strips
    4 spring onions, finely chopped
    140 g (5 oz) sugar snap peas, diagonally sliced
    2 tablespoons toasted sesame seeds
    350 g (12 oz) fresh blackberries or raspberries or
       a combination of both

1. Make the dressing: in a jar with a tightly fitting lid, combine the garlic, ginger, soy sauce, rice vinegar, peanut oil, sesame oil and hot pepper sauce. Close the lid and shake vigorously to combine. Set aside to let the flavours blend.

2. Bring a large pan of water to the boil. Add the Udon noodles, and cook until tender, about 3 minutes. Drain, and place in a serving bowl.

3. In a microwave-safe bowl, combine the green, red and yellow peppers with the spring onions and sugar snap peas. Cook in a microwave until warm, but still crisp. Add to the noodles in the bowl, and pour the dressing over all. Toss to coat in the dressing, then sprinkle toasted sesame seeds and blackberries over the top.

BLACKBERRY RUM

This is a variation of sloe gin, it is made in the same way and needs three months to mature.

You will need: **Makes about 1 litre (1¾ pints)**
    500 g (9 oz) blackberries, mashed
    75 g (2½ oz) granulated sugar
    few drops almond essence
    750 ml (1¼ pints) light rum

1. Put the blackberries, sugar and almond essence into a large jar. Add the rum, seal tightly and store in a dark place for three months, shaking occasionally.

2. After three months strain the liquor through muslin or an all-purpose cloth and re-bottle in a clean 1-litre spirits bottle.

3. Use as you would sloe gin, or for a Champagne cocktail or Kir Royale. Pour 2 tablespoons of blackberry rum into Champagne flutes or cocktail glasses and top up with Champagne or sparkling wine. Or just add to sparkling water for a very refreshing drink with a kick!

BLACKBERRY-LEMON ICE CREAM

Once there was only vanilla, chocolate or strawberry. Now, with an ice-cream maker and a bunch of fresh or frozen berries, you can make your own superb fruit ice creams.

You will need: **Makes about ¾ litre (1¼ pints)**
   115 g (4 oz) fresh or thawed frozen unsweetened
      blackberries, mashed
   200 g (7 oz) sweetened condensed milk
   2 tablespoons freshly squeezed lemon juice
   1 teaspoon grated lemon rind (optional)
   180 ml (6 fl oz) milk
   180 ml (6 fl oz) single cream

1. In a large bowl, combine the blackberries, condensed milk, lemon juice and lemon rind (optional). Stir in the milk and single cream.

2. Pour into an ice-cream freezer container and freeze according to manufacturer's instructions.

3. Remove from the freezer about 20 minutes before serving.

BLACKBERRY MERINGUE FREEZE

This delicious, easy ice cream 'cake' can be made up to one month in advance, then softened for about half an hour in the refrigerator before serving.

You will need: **Serves 10-12**
    600 ml (1 pint) double cream
    55 g (2 oz) light-brown sugar
    2 tablespoons cocoa powder
    4 meringue nests (or homemade meringue)
    450 g (1 lb) fresh blackberries
    Icing sugar to serve
    225 g (8 oz) fresh blackberries to serve

1. In a bowl, whip the cream until it just holds its shape, then stir in the sugar and sift in the cocoa powder. Break up the meringues into small pieces and lightly mash the blackberries with a fork. Fold both into the whipped cream.

2. Line a 23 cm (9 inch) springform tin with clingfilm. Spoon in the blackberry mixture, pressing it into the corners, then smoothing the top. Cover and freeze until firm, at least 4 hours or overnight.

3. About half an hour before serving, transfer the dessert to the refrigerator. To serve, turn out onto a flat serving plate and dust with sifted icing sugar. Cut into wedges and garnish with the remaining blackberries.

CHILLED BLACKBERRY SOUP

You will need: **Makes 4 servings**
225 g (8 oz) blackberries
360 ml (12 fl oz) buttermilk
350 g (12 oz) plain low-fat yogurt
Pinch of salt
Berries to garnish (optional)

1. Sieve the blackberries to remove the seeds and place them in a blender container. Add the buttermilk and the yogurt and add a pinch of salt. Blend thoroughly. Pour into a covered container and refrigerate for at least two hours.

2. Before serving, whisk the soup to combine again and serve cold, garnished with the berries, if using.

BLACKCURRANTS

ARINA'S BLACKCURRANT JAM

My friend Arina makes the most delicious blackcurrant jam and redcurrant jelly. I always hope her berry crop is bountiful.

You will need: **Makes 2 kg (4.4 lb)**
1 kg (2.2 lb) blackcurrants, destalked and washed
1 kg (2.2 lb) sugar

1. Whizz the blackcurrants in a food processor until puréed.

2. Tip into a large saucepan or preserving pan and add the sugar. Stir the mixture. Leave to dissolve for a couple of hours, stirring occasionally. The mixture should turn from pink to a beautiful purple colour.

3. Over a medium heat, bring to the boil, stirring all the time. Remove from the heat.

4. Pour the hot jam carefully into glass jars which have been washed, dried and sterilised (heat in a moderate oven for 5 minutes or in a microwave oven for 1 minute) and seal while still hot. Make sure that the centre of the lid is sucked in once the jar has cooled down.

Arina also does a cold version of this jam. The ratio of fruit to sugar is 1:2 in this case (safe option), 1:1.5 is not so safe but not so sweet. The process is almost the same, just no need to boil — whizz the fruit, add the sugar, leave to dissolve, put in the jars (you don't need to sterilise or seal). The only risk is if the fruit was not fresh enough, it might start to ferment after about a month. So you need to keep checking the jars. If fermenting has started, revert to the hot version of the jam (bring to the boil, pour hot into the sterilised jars and seal). Jam is saved!

BLUEBERRIES

BLUEBERRY FROZEN YOGURT

Frozen yogurt is really quite a virtuous dessert, since it contains far less fat than ice cream. It also has a gorgeous, slightly sharp tang which is very refreshing after dinner.

You will need: **Makes about 900 ml (1½ pints)**
    170 g (6 oz) frozen blueberries, slightly thawed
    300 g (10 oz) plain or vanilla low-fat yogurt
    120 ml (4 fl oz) rich milk or half cream
    115 g (4 oz) caster sugar

1. Mash the berries. Combine with the remaining ingredients, cover and refrigerate until chilled.

2. Start the ice-cream maker and pour the blueberry mixture into it while it is churning. Continue until the frozen yogurt is the correct consistency or the machine stops.

3. Pack the frozen yogurt into a freezer container and freeze until you are ready to serve. If it has frozen hard, you might need to take it out of the freezer 20 minutes before serving.

NOTE: Once you have the consistency right, you can make frozen yogurt with any berry and yogurt combination.

BLUEBERRY VODKA MARTINIS

These blueberry martinis will be the hit of any party! They are simple to make, but the key is the homemade blueberry vodka that requires two weeks to infuse properly.

You will need: **Makes 10 servings**

   225 g (8 oz) fresh blueberries, rinsed and dried
   1 litre (1¾ pints) vodka
   240 ml (8 fl oz) raspberry liqueur (framboise)
   Juice of 1 lime
   Twists of lime, to garnish

1. Start at least two weeks ahead of time. Make the blueberry vodka. Cut a small nick in each of the blueberries and put them into a clean 1-litre spirits bottle. Fill the bottle with vodka to just below the neck and add just enough raspberry liqueur to fill.

2. Cap the bottle and set aside in a dark place for at least two weeks.

3. To make the martinis: in a cocktail shaker filled with ice, combine 2 parts blueberry vodka, 1 part raspberry liqueur and a dash of lime juice. Shake vigorously and strain into a martini glass. Garnish with a twist of lime.

BLUEBERRY WALNUT TEABREAD

This is a delicious teabread for bread machines, containing blueberries, walnuts and a little grated lemon rind for a bit of extra zing.

You will need: **Makes one 900 g (2 lb) loaf**
- 75 g (2½ oz) margarine, softened
- 120 ml (4 fl oz) milk
- 2 large eggs
- 225 g (8 oz) granulated sugar
- 350 g (12 oz) plain flour
- 2½ teaspoons baking powder
- ½ teaspoon bicarbonate of soda
- 1 teaspoon salt
- 140 g (5 oz) fresh or frozen blueberries, thawed
- 55 g (2 oz) chopped walnuts
- ½ teaspoon grated lemon rind

1. In a large bowl, beat together the margarine, milk, eggs and sugar. Stir in the flour, baking powder, bicarbonate of soda and salt. Fold in the blueberries, walnuts and lemon rind.

2. Spray the bread machine pan with cooking spray. Pour the batter into the pan and put the pan into the bread machine. Select the cake cycle. Press start. Check after 10 minutes to see if there is any unmixed flour around the edges. If so, mix it in with a plastic spatula.

3. At the end of the cycle, remove the pan from the machine and run a plastic spatula around the edge of the bread. Turn out onto a wire rack and cool for 20–30 minutes before slicing.

TO DIE FOR BLUEBERRY MUFFINS

You will need: **Makes about 18 muffins**

    115 g (4 oz) sunflower margarine
    280 g (10 oz) granulated sugar
    2 large eggs
    225 g (8 oz) plain low-fat yogurt
    1 teaspoon vanilla essence
    225 g (8 oz) plain flour
    1 teaspoon baking powder
    ½ teaspoon bicarbonate of soda
    ¼ teaspoon salt
    ½ teaspoon ground cinnamon
    125 g (4½ oz) fresh blueberries, rinsed and dried

1. Preheat the oven to 190°C (375°F/Gas Mark 5).

2. In a large mixing bowl, mix the margarine and sugar together until fluffy. Add the eggs and beat until smooth.

3. Mix in the yogurt and vanilla essence.

4. In a medium bowl, combine the flour, baking powder, bicarbonate of soda, salt and cinnamon. Stir into the sugar mixture and carefully fold in the blueberries.

5. Line muffin tins with paper cases or grease them and fill each about three-quarters full. Sprinkle a little sugar over the tops.

6. Bake in the centre of the oven for about 25 minutes, until a toothpick inserted into the centre comes out clean (but don't forget there will be some blueberry juice, so don't overbake).

MICROWAVE BERRY SAUCE

You will need: **Makes about 450 ml (¾ pint)**
115 g (4 oz) granulated sugar
2 tablespoons cornflour
350 g (12 oz) fresh or frozen unsweetened blueberries or
raspberries, thawed
5 tablespoons water
1 teaspoon lemon juice
⅛ teaspoon almond essence (optional)

1. Stir the sugar and cornflour together in a 1-litre
(1¾ pint) glass measuring cup. Mix in the thawed berries
and water, ensuring no dry mixture remains on the
bottom.

2. Cook, uncovered, for 3–5 minutes on full power,
stirring twice during cooking. The sauce should come to
the boil and thicken. Stir in the lemon juice.

Optional:
Add ⅛ teaspoon almond essence to blueberry or
raspberry sauce. Serve over vanilla ice cream or a rich
chocolate dessert.

BOYSENBERRIES

BOYSENBERRY KISS COCKTAIL

A sip of this cocktail is like a kiss, sweet and tender. This
is the perfect drink for a warm summer day.

You will need: **Makes 2 drinks**
90 ml (3 fl oz) vodka
2 teaspoons freshly-squeezed lemon juice
2 tablespoons Chambord (blackberry liqueur)
Crushed ice
Whole boysenberries (or blackberries)
Lemon rind twist for garnish

1. Place the vodka, Chambord, lemon juice and ice in a cocktail shaker, and shake to combine.

2. Strain the mixture into two chilled martini glasses, drop in a fresh boysenberry or two and place a twist of lemon on the rim of the glass.

CAPE GOOSEBERRIES

CAPE GOOSEBERRY SAUCE

You will need: **Makes about 1.8 kg (4 lb)**
   1 kg (2.2 lb) cape gooseberries
   4 onions, sliced
   350 g (12 oz) brown sugar
   300 ml (10 fl oz) cider vinegar
   1 teaspoon ground ginger
   1 teaspoon salt
   Pinch of cayenne pepper

1. Wash the cape gooseberries and drain. Prick each one with a needle.

2. Combine all ingredients in a saucepan and simmer, uncovered for 45 minutes, stirring regularly.

3. Pour into sterilised bottles and allow to cool.

4. Seal when cold and store in a cool place.

CAPE GOOSEBERRY AND PASSION FRUIT JAM

You will need: **Makes about 1 kg (2.2 lb)**
   675 g (1½ lb) cape gooseberries
   Pulp of 4 passion fruit
   120 ml (4 fl oz) water
   450 g (1 lb) granulated sugar

1. In a saucepan cook the cape gooseberries, passion fruit and water for 30 minutes, or until tender.

2. Drain and discard the skins and most of the pips. (You can drain through a jelly bag or muslin to get rid of all the pips.)

3. Return the liquid to the pan, add the sugar and boil fast until setting point is reached.

4. Pack into sterilised jars and seal.

DECORATIVE CAPE GOOSEBERRIES

1. Gather some cape gooseberries that are still in their lanterns. Peel back the lanterns, reflexing them into a star shape.

2. Carefully dip the berry into melted chocolate. Place on greaseproof paper to set. Use to garnish sweet desserts or a cheese board.

CRANBERRIES

CRANBERRY OATMEAL COOKIES

It does take some patience to incorporate the porridge oats into the dough, but the thick and chewy results are worth it.

You will need: **Makes about 25 cookies**

    350 g (12 oz) unsalted butter, room temperature
    400 g (14 oz) light-brown sugar
    2 large eggs
    1½ tablespoons honey
    2 teaspoons vanilla essence
    ½ teaspoon salt
    225 g (8 oz) plain flour
    450 g (1 lb) porridge oats
    350 g (12 oz) fresh cranberries, coarsely chopped
    85 g (3 oz) sultanas
    Finely grated rind of 1 orange
    140 g (5 oz) coarsely chopped walnuts

1. Preheat the oven to 180°C (350°F/Gas Mark 4). Line baking trays with parchment paper.

2. Cream the butter and sugar in a large bowl until smooth. Add the eggs, honey, vanilla essence and salt and beat until smooth and creamy.

3. Using a large wooden spoon or your hands, work in the flour and oats until well-combined. Add the cranberries, sultanas, orange rind, and walnuts; mix until evenly incorporated.

4. With your hands, form the dough on the baking sheets into patties 1 cm (½ inch) thick and 6 to 7.5 cm (2½ to 3 inches) in diameter. Bake the cookies until lightly browned but still a little soft at the centre, 15 to 20 minutes. Cool on wire racks.

CRANBERRY-ORANGE BRUNCH BREAD

A dense bread with the wonderful taste of cranberries, this is wonderful as part of a holiday brunch. And it's easy-peasy made in a breadmaker.

You will need: **Makes one 750 g (1½ lb) loaf**

300 ml (10 fl oz) freshly-squeezed orange juice
2 tablespoons sunflower oil
2 tablespoons honey
1 teaspoon salt
450 g (1 lb) strong bread flour
1 tablespoon dried skimmed milk
½ teaspoon ground cinnamon
½ teaspoon ground allspice
7 g sachet (2 teaspoons) fast-action bread yeast
1 tablespoon grated orange rind
115 g (4 oz) sweetened dried cranberries
40 g (1½ oz) chopped pecans or walnuts

Place ingredients in the pan of the bread machine in the order recommended by the manufacturer. Select basic white cycle and start. If your machine has a fruit setting, add the cranberries and nuts at the signal. Alternatively, add them about 5 minutes before the kneading cycle has finished.

CRANBERRY ORANGE RELISH WITH GINGER

This lovely uncooked relish would go beautifully with any poultry or game meat.

You will need: **Makes about 800 g (1¾lb)**
- 1 large naval orange
- 450 g (1 lb) fresh or frozen cranberries
- 170 g (6 oz) granulated sugar
- 2 teaspoons fresh ginger, grated
- 2–3 tablespoons orange liqueur (optional)

1. Grate 1 teaspoon of the orange rind and tip into a food processor or blender. Peel the orange and discard the remainder of the rind. Chop the orange flesh coarsely and add that to the food processor.

2. Chop the cranberries coarsely and add to the processor with the ginger and the orange liqueur, if using.

3. Blend until just combined, keeping some of the texture. Pour into jars, cover and refrigerate until needed.

CRANBERRY VINAIGRETTE

You will need: **Makes about 300 ml (10 fl oz)**
- 115 g (4 oz) flaked almonds
- 3 tablespoons red wine vinegar
- 5 tablespoons extra virgin olive oil
- 55g (2 oz) fresh cranberries
- 1 tablespoon Dijon mustard
- ½ teaspoon finely chopped garlic
- ½ teaspoon salt
- ½ teaspoon freshly ground black pepper
- 2 tablespoons water

Place all ingredients in a food processor and process until smooth. Pour into a clean screw-top jar and store any leftover dressing in the refrigerator.

This salad dressing is especially nice with salad leaves and crumbled feta cheese.

CRANBERRY WHITE CHOCOLATE FUDGE

You will need: **Makes 64 pieces**
30 g (1 oz) unsalted butter
150 ml (5 fl oz) evaporated milk
350 g (12 oz) caster sugar
½ teaspoon salt
115 g (4 oz) mini marshmallows
1 teaspoon vanilla essence
250 g (9 oz) good-quality white chocolate chips or white chocolate bar, chopped
115 g (4 oz) dried cranberries
55 g (2 oz) chopped walnuts (optional)
Rind of 1 orange, grated

1. Grease a 20 cm (8 inch) square pan and line with parchment paper.

2. In a medium saucepan, combine the butter, milk, sugar and salt. Bring to the boil over a medium heat, stirring constantly for 5 minutes. Remove from the heat. Stir in the marshmallows, vanilla essence, chocolate chips, dried cranberries, nuts if using and orange rind. Stir quickly for 1 minute until the marshmallows melt and blend into the mixture.

3. Pour into the prepared pan, cool and cut into squares.

SPICED CRANBERRY RELISH

This is a more unusual relish in that it is cooked, and it might be a welcome change served with a cheese course.

You will need: **Makes about 1 litre (1¾ pints)**
225 g (8 oz) granulated sugar
1 onion, finely chopped
6 whole cloves
1 teaspoon ground cinnamon
Seeds of 2 whole cardamom pods, crushed
Pinch of cayenne pepper

¼ teaspoon ground ginger
½ teaspoon salt
4 tablespoons cider vinegar
225 g (8 oz) fresh cranberries
170 g (6 oz) seedless raisins
75 g (2 ½ oz) brown sugar
240 ml (8 fl oz) water

1. Combine all the ingredients in a large saucepan and bring to the boil.

2. Reduce the heat to a simmer and cook for 45 minutes.

3. Put into clean jars and refrigerate. Serve chilled.

ELDERBERRIES

Elderberries should not be eaten raw. All parts of the plant contain small amounts of the toxin hydrocyanic acid, which is destroyed by ordinary cooking.

ELDERBERRY CORDIAL

You will need:
Elderberries (still on stalks)
Sugar, white granulated
Cloves

1. Pick the fruit on a dry day and stew with the stalks in a large stainless steel saucepan, with just enough water to cover for 30–40 minutes until the fruit is really soft. Remove from the heat and allow to cool.

2. Strain the elderberries through muslin, squeezing to get out all of the juice.

3. Put back into the rinsed-out saucepan. To each ½ litre (17 fl oz) of juice add 450 g (1 lb) of white granulated sugar and 10 cloves. Boil for 10 minutes. Remove from the heat and allow to cool.

4. Bottle in sterilised bottles with good-quality plastic screw-on tops, making sure you distribute the cloves evenly amongst the bottles (they act as a preservative).

5. The cordial can be used immediately, or it will keep well for a year or two. Taken with hot water it is renowned as a guard against colds, and a glass a day throughout winter is a wise precaution.

ELDERBERRY PIE

You will need: Serves 6

    300 g (10 oz) ripe fresh elderberries
    115 g (4 oz) granulated sugar
    Pinch of salt
    3 tablespoons freshly squeezed lemon juice
    2 tablespoons plain flour
    1 tablespoon unsalted butter, diced
    Unbaked shortcrust pastry for a 2-crust pie

1. In a bowl, mix the elderberries, sugar, salt and lemon juice. Sprinkle with flour and dot with butter.

2. Preheat the oven to 180°C (350°F/Gas Mark 4). Divide the pastry into two pieces, with one slightly larger than the other. Roll out the larger piece to fit a 20 cm (8 inch) pie tin and ease it into the tin, slightly overlapping over the sides.

3. Put the elderberry filling into the prepared pie tin and roll out the top crust. Carefully cover the pie with the crust and press the edges together, either with a fork or your fingers. Cut a few slits in the top crust for the steam to escape.

4. Bake for 30 minutes until the crust is golden-brown.

5. Serve warm with a scoop of vanilla ice cream.

ELDERBERRY WINE

This is a more ambitious recipe utilising elderberries. If you are new to winemaking, to find out about some of these lesser-known ingredients or methods, either go to a shop that caters to home winemaking, or look them up on the Internet.

You will need:
  3.5 litres (6 pints) water
  900 g (2 lb) caster sugar
  1.35 kg (3 lb) ripe fresh elderberries
  2 teaspoons acid blend
  1 teaspoon yeast nutrient (see below)
  1 crushed Campden tablet (see below)
  ½ teaspoon pectic enzyme (see below)
  Montrachet wine yeast

1. In a large pan, bring the water to the boil and stir in the sugar until dissolved.

2. Meanwhile, wash, inspect and destalk the elderberries. Put them in a nylon straining bag, tie it closed and put into a primary fermentation vessel.

3. Wearing sterilised rubber gloves, mash the elderberries and cover with the boiling sugared water. Cover and set aside to cool. When the mixture is lukewarm, add the acid blend, yeast nutrient and Campden tablet. Cover the primary and wait 12 hours, then stir in the pectic enzyme. Re-cover the primary and wait another 12 hours, then add the yeast. Cover and stir daily, gently squeezing the bag to extract the flavour from the berries. (Don't forget the gloves or you'll be sorry). Ferment 14 days, then drip drain the elderberries (don't squeeze).

4. Combine the drippings with the juice and set aside overnight. Rack into a secondary vessel and fit airlock. Put into a cool, dark place to protect from the light. Ferment two months and rack, top up and refit airlock.

5. Repeat two months later and again, two months after that. Stabilise and wait 10 days.

6. Rack, sweeten to taste and bottle. Store bottles in a dark place for one year. Then enjoy.

CAMPDEN TABLETS

Tablets used in winemaking to sanitise equipment and fermentation media and add free SO_2 (sulphur dioxide) to the must or wine. When crushed and dissolved, they provide SO_2 in a convenient form. Tablets must be crushed to use, but this ensures the proper dosage and assists in their dissolution. The active ingredient in Campden tablets can be purchased in bulk from most winemaker suppliers under its chemical name, potassium metabisulfite. For sanitising bottles, primaries, secondaries, funnels and other equipment, two crushed tablets dissolved in 3.75 litres (8 pints) of water will suffice. Do not rinse equipment after sanitising. For adding to must, use one crushed and dissolved tablet per 3.75 litres (8 pints) of must and wait 12 hours before adding yeast. Campden tablets come in various sizes and doses, so ask if they are not packaged with instructions. Most tablets are intended to dose 5 US gallons (19 litres) or 5 Imperial gallons (23 litres).

PECTIC ENZYME

This increases juice yields from fruits by breaking down the cellular structure. Also acts as a clarifier, and is used to clear hazes caused by residual pectins.

YEAST NUTRIENT

Food for the yeast, containing nitrogenous matter, yeast-tolerant acid, vitamins and certain minerals. While sugar is the main food of the yeast, nutrients are the 'growth hormones', so to speak.

(Adapted from Terry Garey's *The Joy of Home Winemaking*) http://winemaking.jackkeller.net

PONTACK SAUCE

You will need: **Makes about 1 litre (1¾ pints)**
600 ml (1 pint) dry red wine
280 g (10 oz) ripe fresh elderberries, destalked
1 teaspoon salt
1 blade of mace
40 peppercorns
12 cloves
1 onion, finely chopped
Pinch of ginger

1. In a saucepan bring the red wine to the boil. Remove from the heat.

2. Put the elderberries in a casserole dish and pour the wine over. Cover and put in a very low oven 100°C (200°F/Gas Mark ¼) overnight.

3. The next day, pour the contents of the casserole into a saucepan and add the salt, mace, peppercorns, cloves, onion and ginger. Bring to the boil and boil for 10 minutes.

4. Remove from the heat and pour into sterilised bottles. This will keep for at least a year, probably several. It has a fruity taste and goes well with liver and game.

GOJI BERRIES

AMCHI'S CARROT SOUP WITH GOJI BERRIES, ORANGE AND GINGER

Pale brown, knobbly fresh ginger adds a note of exotic, sweet spiciness to soups and other dishes. Look for smooth, shiny ginger with no cracks in the skin. Before slicing, chopping or grating, remove the thin skin using a sharp knife or a vegetable peeler. To grate fresh ginger, use the finest rasps on a standard handheld grater or use a specially designed ginger grater — a small, flat ceramic or light metal tool with tiny, very sharp teeth.

You will need: Serves 4-6

  1 tablespoon olive oil
  2 tablespoons coconut oil
  2 leeks, including tender green portions, thinly sliced
  6 carrots, about 450 g (1 lb), peeled and thinly sliced
  1 red potato, about 225 g (½ lb), peeled and coarsely diced
  1½ teaspoons peeled and finely-chopped or grated fresh ginger
  1 litre (1¾ pints) chicken or vegetable stock
  120 ml (4 fl oz) freshly squeezed orange juice
  2 teaspoons grated orange rind
  55 g (2 oz) goji berries (soaked, if dried)
  Salt and freshly ground white pepper, to taste
  Thin orange slices for garnish (optional)
  Fresh mint sprigs for garnish (optional)

1. In a large saucepan over a medium heat, warm the olive and coconut oils. Add the leeks and sauté until just slightly softened, about 3 minutes. Add the carrots, potato and ginger and sauté until the vegetables are just softened, about 5 minutes more. Add the stock, cover partially and simmer until the vegetables are completely softened, about 20 minutes. Remove from the heat and add the goji berries.

2. In a blender or food processor, purée the soup in batches, leaving some texture, and return the soup to the pan. Alternatively, process with a stick blender in the pan until the desired consistency is reached.

3. Set the pan over a medium heat and stir in the orange juice and rind. Season with salt and white pepper. Ladle the soup into warmed bowls and garnish each serving with an orange slice and a sprig of mint.

Serving tip:
For an alternative garnish, top the soup with fried ginger. Peel a 12.5 cm (5 inch) piece of ginger and slice it into a very fine julienne. In a small frying pan over a medium-high heat, pour in vegetable oil to a depth of about 1 cm (½ inch). When the oil is hot, fry the julienned ginger until crisp and golden-brown, 20–30 seconds. With a slotted spoon transfer the ginger to a plate or tray covered with a sheet of kitchen paper. When cool, divide the ginger into 4–6 portions and use to garnish each serving of soup.

GOJI COCONUT CREAM SAUCE

Bursting with intense red colour, this yummy nutritious sauce makes any fruit, salad or dessert dish a work of art. If you can't get the children to eat their greens, just try this as a salad dressing.

You will need: **Makes about 400 ml (14 fl oz)**
   55 g (2 oz) dried goji berries, soaked in water to cover
   55 g (2 oz) fresh raspberries
   1 cup fresh coconut flesh
   2 pitted dates
   ½ teaspoon orange rind
   Enough coconut milk to turn over in blender

1. Combine all of the ingredients in a blender and blend at high speed until creamy. Pour into a lidded jar and refrigerate until needed. The sauce will keep for up to 3 days in the refrigerator.

2. To make a drink instead of a sauce, add coconut water or purified water.

3. For an incredible exotic dessert variation, substitute mango for the raspberries, and add 1 banana, ¼ teaspoon cinnamon, ½ teaspoon vanilla essence, 1 tablespoon grated ginger and blend without added water.

GOOSEBERRIES

GOOSEBERRY FOOL

You will need: Serves 4

    30 g (1 oz) butter
    450 g (1 lb) gooseberries
    2 tablespoons sugar
    360 ml (12 fl oz) double cream

1. Melt the butter in a heavy saucepan and add the gooseberries and sugar. Cover the saucepan and cook over a low heat until the gooseberries are soft and mushy, about 30 minutes.

2. Remove the gooseberries from the saucepan and beat to a pulp with a wooden spoon. Pass the pulp through a sieve, discarding the skins and pips. Taste the gooseberries and if too tart, add more sugar. Set aside and allow to cool.

3. Whip the cream and gently fold into the gooseberry pulp. Divide equally among small dessert glasses. Chill for at least two hours before serving.

JUNIPER BERRIES

PORK WITH APPLES AND JUNIPER BERRIES

You will need: Serves 4

    2 tablespoons mild olive oil
    1 kg (2.2 lb) diced boneless pork
    500 ml (16 fl oz) apple juice
    200 ml (7 fl oz) dry white wine
    ½ pork stock cube, crumbled
    1 tablespoon finely chopped fresh thyme
    1 tablespoon juniper berries
    2 cooking apples, peeled, cored and sliced
    120 ml (4 fl oz) soured cream*

1. Preheat the oven to 160°C (325°F/Gas Mark 3).

2. Heat the oil in a heavy frying pan and brown the pork all over in batches, removing the browned pork to a plate as it is ready.

3. Tip the pork and any liquid in the plate into a casserole dish. Pour the apple juice into the frying pan, stirring to loosen the browned bits remaining in the pan. Pour over the pork and add the wine, crumbled stock cube, thyme, juniper berries and apples. Bring to the boil on the hob, cover and transfer the casserole to the oven.

4. Oven braise for 1½ hours until the pork is very tender, making sure there is always liquid in the casserole. If necessary, top up with apple juice, wine or water.

5. Just before serving, stir in the soured cream and accompany with buttered noodles and green vegetables.

*Or sour the cream by adding ½ tablespoon lemon juice to 120 ml (4 fl oz) double cream.

ROASTED POUSSINS WITH JUNIPER, CARAMELISED ROOT VEGETABLES AND DRIED CURRANT SAUCE

Be sure to start marinating the poussins at least six hours ahead.

Caramelised root vegetables: **Serves 6**
> 3 tablespoons butter
> 2 tablespoons olive oil
> 1 large onion, coarsely chopped
> 2 medium swedes, peeled, cut into .5 cm (¼-inch) cubes
> 2 medium turnips, peeled, cut into .5 cm (¼-inch) cubes
> 2 large carrots, peeled, cut into .5 cm (¼-inch) cubes
> 2 large parsnips, peeled, cut into .5 cm (¼-inch) cubes
> 4 stalks celery, diced
> 400 g (14 oz) tinned whole roasted peeled chestnuts, halved
> 6 cloves garlic, finely chopped
> 2 tablespoons chopped fresh thyme

Poussins:

    3 tablespoons chopped fresh thyme
    4 tablespoons chopped shallots
    4 tablespoons olive oil
    1 ½ tablespoons finely-grated orange rind
    4 cloves garlic, finely chopped
    1 tablespoon juniper berries, crushed in mortar with pestle
    6 poussins, thawed if frozen

    360 ml (12 fl oz) chicken stock
    Freshly-ground black pepper
    Salt

    4 tablespoons dried currants

1. Prepare the vegetables: melt butter with the oil in a very large pan over a medium-high heat. Add the onion; sauté for 5 minutes. Add the swedes, carrots, turnips, parsnips and celery. Sauté until vegetables are caramelised and tender, stirring often, about 30 minutes. Stir in the chestnuts, garlic and thyme; sauté for 5 minutes. Season generously with salt and pepper. This can be done one day ahead. Cover and chill. Before serving, re-warm a over a medium heat, stirring frequently, until heated through.

2. Prepare the poussins: mix 2 tablespoons of the thyme, shallots, olive oil, orange rind, garlic and crushed juniper berries in a small bowl for the marinade. Rub the marinade all over the poussins. Place them in a large roasting tin; cover and refrigerate at least 6 hours or overnight.

3. Preheat the oven to 160°C (325°F/Gas Mark 3). Pour the chicken stock into the roasting tin with the poussins. Season with pepper. Cover tin tightly with foil. Roast until the poussins are cooked through and juices run clear when thighs are pierced with fork, about 1 hour 15 minutes. Remove from the oven. Preheat the grill.

4. Pour pan juices from the poussins into a small saucepan; add dried currants and remaining 1 tablespoon of thyme. Boil until the liquid is reduced to about 240 ml

(8 fl oz), about 5 minutes (sauce will be thin). Season sauce to taste with salt and pepper.

5. Meanwhile, grill poussins until lightly browned, watching closely to avoid burning, about 4 minutes.

6. Place one poussin on each plate. Divide caramelised vegetables among plates. Spoon sauce over poussins and serve.

LOGANBERRIES
LOGANBERRY-LEMON CURD BARS

You will need: **Makes 12-16**

125 g (4½ oz) plain flour
115 g (4 oz) unsalted butter, melted
5 tablespoons icing sugar

Filling:

2 eggs
1 teaspoon freshly-grated lemon peel
3 tablespoons freshly-squeezed lemon juice
225 g (8 oz) granulated sugar
2 tablespoons plain flour
¼ teaspoon baking powder
175 g (6 oz) fresh loganberries
Icing sugar

A 2.5 cm (1 inch) deep non-stick 23 cm (9 inch) square tin works best, but use a plastic knife to cut the bars into squares so that you don't scratch the non-stick surface of the tin.

The recipe combines tangy lemon curd with juicy, tart, loganberries, held together by a sweet, crumbly crust. If you can't find loganberries, substitute blackberries or blueberries.

1. Preheat the oven to 180°C (350°F/Gas Mark 4). Sift together the flour and sugar in a large bowl. Add the melted butter and combine the mixture into a loose dough. Pat the mixture into a non-stick baking tin.

2. Bake the pastry until just browned around the edges, about 10 minutes. Remove from the oven and set aside.

3. In a mixing bowl, add the eggs, lemon peel, lemon juice and sugar. Beat at low speed until the mixture is thick and smooth, about 5 minutes. Combine the flour and baking powder in a bowl. With the mixer running, add the flour and baking powder and mix until well blended, about 3 minutes. Pour the filling into the pre-baked pastry base. Place the whole loganberries evenly throughout the filling.

4. Bake the loganberry-lemon curd mixture in the oven for about 20 minutes, or until the filling is set.

5. Remove from the oven and let the tin cool on a rack for 30 minutes. Sift the icing sugar over the top of the cooled filling. Cut into bars and serve with crème fraîche or vanilla ice cream.

MARIONBERRIES

MARIONBERRY COBBLER

In this recipe, we bake marionberries (blackberries can be substituted) underneath a scone blanket and serve it warm with a scoop of vanilla ice cream — a quintessentially American dessert. This recipe is adapted from a recipe provided by the Oregon Raspberry and Blackberry Commission.

Cobbler: Serves 4
    450 g (1 lb) fresh or frozen marionberries and their juice
    170 g (6 oz) granulated sugar
    2 tablespoons plain flour
    2 teaspoons freshly squeezed lemon juice

Scone topping:
    170 g (6 oz) plain flour
    1 teaspoon baking powder
    ¼ teaspoon bicarbonate of soda
    1 tablespoon granulated sugar
    55 g (2 oz) unsalted butter
    240 ml (8 fl oz) buttermilk or soured milk*

    Vanilla ice cream to serve

1. Preheat the oven to 180°C (350°F/Gas Mark 4).

2. In a large bowl, combine the marionberries and their juice, sugar, flour and lemon juice. Gently toss the berries to combine with the other ingredients. Spoon the berry mixture into a deep, 20 cm (8 inch) square ceramic baking dish. Bake for 20 minutes. As the berry mixture is baking, prepare the scone topping.

3. In a food processor, add the flour, baking powder, bicarbonate of soda and sugar and process to combine. Add the butter to the flour mixture and process until the butter is the size of small peas. With the processor running, add enough of the buttermilk to make a moist dough.

4. Remove the berry mixture from the oven. Keep the oven turned on. Drop large spoonfuls of the dough evenly onto the top of the berry mixture. Return the cobbler to the oven and bake for 20 minutes, until the scones have risen and are golden-brown.

5. Remove the cobbler from the oven and let it cool on a rack until it is just warm. Serve topped with a scoop of vanilla ice cream.

*To sour milk, add 2 tablespoons lemon juice to 200 ml (7 fl oz) milk and set aside until it thickens and curdles slightly.

MULBERRIES

MULBERRY ALMOND MUFFINS

This is a wonderful treat if you have any mulberry preserves. If not, raspberry jam would work very well.

You will need: **Makes 16**

    115 g (4 oz) butter at room temperature
    170 g (6 oz) sugar
    2 large eggs
    1 teaspoon almond essence
    225 g (8 oz) plain flour
    1 teaspoon baking powder
    ½ teaspoon bicarbonate of soda
    ½ teaspoon salt
    225 g (8 oz) plain yogurt
    4 tablespoons mulberry preserves
    140 g (5 oz) almond paste, cut into 16 pieces

1. Preheat the oven to 180°C (350°F/Gas Mark 4). Line 16 muffin cups with paper liners.

2. In a large bowl, beat the butter until creamy. Beat in the sugar until pale and fluffy. Whisk in the eggs, one at a time.

3. In another bowl, mix the flour, baking powder, bicarbonate of soda and salt together.

4. Add the flour to the creamed mixture, alternating with the yogurt, beginning and ending with the flour.

5. Pat the almond paste into discs, about 4 cm (1½ inches) in diameter.

6. Spoon about 2 tablespoons of the batter into each muffin cup, smooth the top, add 1 teaspoon of mulberry preserves, 1 almond paste disc and another 2 tablespoons of batter.

7. Bake for 25–30 minutes or until lightly browned. Remove from the oven, turn out onto a wire rack and leave to stand for at least 10 minutes. Store any leftover muffins in an airtight container.

MULBERRY CRUMBLE

Fruit layer: Serves 6

    675 g (1½ lb) mulberries

    120 ml (4 fl oz) freshly-squeezed orange juice

    2 tablespoons arrowroot

    1½ tablespoons chopped fresh spearmint or other mint

    2 teaspoons vanilla essence

    ½ teaspoon almond essence

    2 tablespoons mild honey

Crumble topping:

    225 g (8 oz) fresh breadcrumbs

    4 tablespoons corn oil or flaxseed oil

    115 g (4 oz) unsalted pistachio nuts or almonds, chopped

    Pinch of salt

    1 teaspoon ground cinnamon

1. Preheat the oven to 180°C (350°F/Gas Mark 4).

2. Make the fruit layer. Combine all the ingredients in a bowl and pour the mixture into a 3-litre (5-pint) baking dish.

3. Make the topping. Combine all the ingredients except the cinnamon. Press the crumble on top of the fruit layer and sprinkle with the cinnamon.

4. Bake for 40 minutes and serve hot or cold.

MULBERRY SORBET

You will need: **Makes 1 litre (1¾ pints)**

675 g (1½ lb) ripe fresh mulberries
450 g (1 lb) sugar
450 ml (15 fl oz) fresh buttermilk*
Fresh mulberries and fresh mint sprigs to garnish

1. In a bowl, stir the mulberries and sugar together. Let them stand for 30 minutes.

2. Purée the mulberry mixture in a food processor or blender until smooth, stopping to scrape down the sides if necessary.

3. Pour through a fine sieve into a bowl, pressing to extract as much juice as possible. Discard the solids and add the buttermilk to the mulberry mixture. Mix well and pour into a 23-cm (9-inch) square tin. Cover and freeze for 8 hours.

4. Break up the frozen mixture into chunks and place in a bowl. Beat with an electric mixer at a medium speed until smooth. Return to the tin, cover and freeze for 3 hours, or until firm.

5. To serve, spoon into dessert glasses and garnish with fresh mulberries and mint sprigs.

*To sour milk, add 2 tablespoons lemon juice to 200 ml (7 fl oz) milk and set aside until it thickens and curdles slightly.

RASPBERRIES

RASPBERRY CURD

You will need: **Makes about 675 g (1½ lb)**
   115 g (4 oz) unsalted butter
   350 g (12 oz) ripe fresh raspberries
   5 large egg yolks, lightly whisked
   175 g (6 oz) caster sugar
   Pinch of salt
   1 tablespoon freshly-squeezed lemon juice

1. Melt the butter in a large saucepan over a medium heat. Add the raspberries, egg yolks, sugar and salt and cook, mashing the berries and stirring constantly until thick, about 10 minutes.

2. Pour the mixture through a coarse sieve set over a bowl, pressing hard on the solids to extract as much liquid as possible. Cool to room temperature. The curd will continue to thicken as it cools. Stir in the lemon juice and refrigerate, covered until ready to serve or for up to 1 month.

MARION'S RASPBERRY TRIFLE

This is a lovely light trifle, originally made by my husband's goddaughter's grandmother and now faithfully and lovingly recreated by her.

You will need: **Serves 6–8**
   4 trifle sponges or 450 g (1 lb) sponge or pound cake
   175 g (6 oz) raspberry jam, preferably homemade
   500 g (18 oz) homemade custard or bought fresh vanilla custard
   300 ml (10 fl oz) double cream
   225 g (8 oz) fresh raspberries
   150 ml (5 fl oz) framboise liqueur
   1 tablespoon grated plain chocolate
   30 g (1 oz) flaked almonds, lightly toasted

1. Slice the trifle sponges in half or slice sponge or pound cake. Spread liberally with the jam and fit on the bottom

of the glass trifle bowl. Cover with a layer of raspberries and sprinkle with the framboise liqueur. Cover with the cold custard.

2. Lightly whip the cream and spread over the custard. Sprinkle with the grated chocolate and toasted almonds.

3. Chill, covered, in the refrigerator for at least two hours or overnight.

RASPBERRY VINAIGRETTE

This vibrant and colourful raspberry vinaigrette is a great choice to serve on a nutty or fruity salad. For an even better treat, toss a handful of cranberries, pine nuts or walnuts on your salad.

You will need: **Makes about 300 ml (10 fl oz)**

   85 g (3 oz) raspberries, fresh or frozen
   4 tablespoons apple cider vinegar
   4 tablespoons white balsamic vinegar
   2 teaspoons sugar
   1 tablespoon Dijon mustard
   4 tablespoons grapeseed oil

Add all ingredients, except the oil, to a blender or food processor and purée until smooth. Slowly add the oil until well combined. Pour into a clean screw-top jar. Store any leftover dressing in the refrigerator.

RASPBERRY PINE NUT MUFFINS

I've had these muffins in Starbucks, but in my opinion, the homemade ones are even better! Serve them during a coffee morning. They will be much appreciated.

You will need: **Makes 12**

   2 teaspoons instant coffee granules
   1 tablespoon hot milk
   400 g (14 oz) self-raising flour
   55 g (2 oz) pine nuts, toasted lightly
   170 g (6 oz) caster sugar
   1 teaspoon bicarbonate of soda
   115 g (4 oz) unsalted butter, melted
   2 large eggs
   280 g (10 oz) plain yogurt or soured cream
   250 g (9 oz) fresh raspberries

1. Preheat the oven to 200°C (400°F/Gas Mark 6). Line a 12-cup muffin tin with paper liners.

2. In a cup, dissolve the coffee in the hot milk and set aside to cool.

3. In a large bowl, mix the flour, half the pine nuts, sugar and bicarbonate of soda.

4. In another bowl, beat the butter with the eggs, then add the yogurt or soured cream and the cooled coffee. Stir this into the flour mixture until it is just combined, tip in the raspberries and fold to mix. Don't overbeat or the mixture will toughen.

5. Fill the muffin cups with the batter — they will be full. Poke the rest of the pine nuts more or less evenly into the muffins and bake for 25 minutes, until the muffins have risen and are golden-brown.

6. Remove from the oven and let them cool in the muffin tin for about 10 minutes, then turn out onto a wire rack. They are best eaten within a few days.

RAZZMATAZZ

You will need: **Makes 2 drinks**
  180 ml (6 fl oz) pineapple juice
  12 fresh raspberries
  1 ripe banana
  Crushed ice

Mix all ingredients together in a blender until smooth.
Pour into tall glasses and serve.

REDCURRANTS

REDCURRANT AND SAGE GRAVY

A simple, aromatic gravy for turkey, chicken or pork.

You will need: **Serves 8**
  Pan juices reserved from roasted meat (or 1 tablespoon
    vegetable oil and 1 chopped onion)
  900 ml (1½ pints) chicken stock, plus extra for thinning
    gravy
  1 tablespoon redcurrant jelly (optional)
  3 tablespoons chopped fresh sage leaves
  3 tablespoons water
  2 tablespoons cornflour
  1 punnet fresh red currants, stemmed

1. Sieve the pan juices into a saucepan. If you're not
using pan juices heat the oil in a saucepan and fry the
onion on a medium heat until browned, about 10
minutes. Add the stock to either the onions or the pan
juices; whichever you are using. Add the jelly, if using,
and bring to the boil, whisking lightly. Stir in the sage
leaves, reduce the heat and simmer.

2. In a small bowl, whisk together the water and
cornflour, then gradually add it to the gravy whisking
constantly to prevent lumps. Add the fresh redcurrants.
Simmer the gravy for 5 minutes to thicken and, if
necessary, add additional stock to thin it. Season to taste
with salt and pepper before serving.

REDCURRANT PARFAIT

Easy to make and a great contrast for those tart summer currants.

You will need: **Serves 4**

    3 teaspoons unflavoured gelatine
    750 ml (1¼ pints) cold blackcurrant juice
    5 tablespoons granulated sugar
    240 ml (8 fl oz) cold double cream
    2 handfuls redcurrants, stemmed

1. Stir the gelatine and 250 ml (8 fl oz) of the chilled juice together in a medium bowl and let sit for 3 minutes.

2. Bring the remaining juice and the sugar just to the boil in a small saucepan.

3. Stir the juice into the gelatine mixture and refrigerate until set, about 1 hour.

4. Whisk the cream to form soft peaks. Layer the set jelly, whipped cream and fresh currants in four dessert glasses and serve.

SUGAR-CRUSTED CURRANT SCONES

You will need: **Makes 12**

    450 g (1 lb) plain flour
    1½ tablespoons baking powder
    ½ teaspoon bicarbonate of soda
    115 g (4 oz) granulated sugar
    ¾ teaspoon salt
    2 teaspoons ground cinnamon
    225 g (8 oz) butter, cut into pieces
    115 g (4 oz) dried currants
    1 teaspoon vanilla essence
    1 large egg
    150 g (5 fl oz) half cream, condensed milk or buttermilk

Topping:
>   45 g (1½ oz) butter, melted
>   115 g (4 oz sugar)

1. Preheat the oven to 220°C (425°F/Gas Mark 7). Grease a large baking sheet or cover it with parchment paper.

2. In a large bowl, stir together the flour, baking powder, bicarbonate of soda, sugar, salt and cinnamon. Use a pastry blender to cut the butter into the dry ingredients, continuing until the mixture is the consistency of coarse breadcrumbs. Stir in the currants.

3. In another bowl, stir together the vanilla essence, egg and milk. Form a well in the centre of the dry ingredients and pour in the liquid mixture. Stir to combine then remove to a floured work surface and knead until combined. Do not over-knead as this will make the scones tough by developing the gluten in the flour.

4. Divide the dough into two pieces and press each into 2-cm (¾-inch) circles. Cut each circle into six wedges and place them on the prepared baking sheet.

5. Melt the butter for the topping and brush on the scones. Sprinkle with the sugar.

6. Bake the scones for 15–18 minutes or until the tops are lightly browned. Remove from the oven and put on a wire rack to cool.

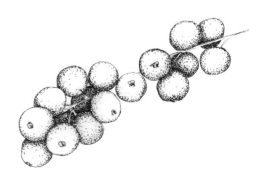

ROSEHIPS

ROSEHIP JELLY

You will need: **Makes about 2 kg (2.2 lb)**

- 1.8 kg (4 lb) ripe rose hips
- 2 litres (3½ pints) water
- 120 ml (4 fl oz) lemon juice
- 1 package pectin crystals
- 1.1 kg (2½ lb) sugar

1. In a large saucepan or preserving pan, simmer the rosehips in water until soft. Crush to mash, and strain through a jelly bag. Should make about 900 ml (1½ pints) of rosehip juice.

2. Add the lemon juice and pectin crystals and stir until the mixture comes to a hard boil. Stir in the sugar all at once. Bring to a full rolling boil and boil for 1 minute, stirring constantly. Remove the jelly from the heat and skim off foam with a metal spoon.

3. Pour into hot sterilised jars.

ROSE HIP PECAN PIE

Pastry: **Serves 6**

- 140 g (5 oz) plain flour
- 85 g (3 oz) cold unsalted butter, cut into 1-cm (½-inch) cubes
- 30 g (1 oz) cold solid vegetable fat
- ¼ teaspoon salt
- 3-4 tablespoons ice water

Filling:

- 115 g (4 oz) dried rosehips
- 4 tablespoons milk
- 170g (6 oz) plain flour
- 2 teaspoons baking powder
- Pinch of salt
- 115 g (4 oz) butter or solid vegetable fat
- 400 g (14 oz) soft brown sugar

2 egg yolks, beaten
2 egg whites
Pecan halves (optional)

1. Prepare the pastry. Blend together the flour, butter, vegetable fat and salt in a bowl with your fingertips or a pastry blender (or pulse in a food processor) until most of mixture resembles coarse breadcrumbs with some small (roughly pea-size) butter lumps. Drizzle evenly with 3 tablespoons of iced water and gently stir with a fork (or pulse in processor) until incorporated.

2. Squeeze a small handful: if it doesn't hold together, add more ice water, 1 tablespoon at a time, stirring (or pulsing) until incorporated, then test again. (Do not overwork mixture, or the pastry will be tough.)

3. Turn the mixture out onto a work surface and divide into 4 portions. With the heel of your hand, smear each portion once or twice in a forward motion to help distribute the fat. Gather the dough together with a scraper and press into a ball, then flatten into a 12.5-cm (5-inch) disk. Wrap in cling film and chill until firm, at least 1 hour. The dough can remain chilled in the refrigerator for up to 1 week.

4. When you are ready to make the pie, preheat the oven to 180°C (350°F/Gas Mark 4). Take the pastry from the refrigerator, roll it out to 27.5 cm (11 inches) and carefully transfer it to a pie tin.

5. In a bowl, soften the rosehips in the milk. In another bowl, sift together the flour, baking powder and salt. Cream in the butter or fat and brown sugar, mixing well. This makes a crumbly mixture — reserve about one-third of the mixture (240 ml/8 fl oz measure) for the topping. To the remainder add the egg yolks, milk and rose hips.

6. Whisk the egg whites until stiff. Fold into the berry mixture. Spoon into the pie tin and sprinkle with the crumbly topping. Garnish with pecan halves if you wish. Bake for 35-45 minutes or until pie is set and the pastry is golden.

ROSEHIP NUT QUICK BREAD

You will need: **Makes one 900 g (2 lb) loaf**
    Juice of 1 orange plus enough water to make
      240 ml (8 fl oz)
    85 g (3 oz) raisins, chopped
    85 g (3 oz) deseeded and chopped wild rosehips
    2 tablespoons melted butter
    1 teaspoon vanilla essence
    1 large egg, beaten
    170 g (6 oz) plain flour
    225 g (8 oz) granulated sugar
    1 teaspoon baking powder
    ½ teaspoon bicarbonate of soda
    ¼ teaspoon salt
    55 g (2 oz) nuts or sunflower seeds

1. In a large bowl, mix the orange juice, raisins, rosehips, butter, vanilla essence and egg. Sift together and then add the dry ingredients. Mix until well blended, but do not overmix or the bread will be dry and heavy. Gently stir in the nuts or sunflower seeds.

2. Preheat the oven to 180°C (350°F/Gas Mark 4). Spoon the batter into a well-greased 900 g (2 lb) loaf tin and bake for 1 hour, until a toothpick inserted into the centre of the bread comes out clean.

ROSEHIP SOUP

This soup, which unusually for a fruit soup is served hot, is very popular in Sweden.

You will need: **Serves 5-6**
    900 ml (1½ pints) rosehip juice*
    2–4 tablespoons honey
    1–3 tablespoons lemon juice or homemade cider vinegar
    1 tablespoon potato starch, cornflour or tapioca
    5–6 tablespoons soured cream or yogurt

1. Heat the rose hip juice, honey and lemon juice or vinegar. Adjust the amounts of honey and lemon juice or vinegar to give a lively sweet, tart flavour.

2. Mix the starch or tapioca in enough cold water to moisten it, and stir it in. Cook until the soup thickens slightly and clears.

3. Serve hot, floating a spoonful of soured cream or yogurt in each bowl.

*From 1.8 kg (4 lb) ripe rose hips (see recipe for Rosehip Jelly on page 141)

SLOES

SLOE GIN

There are many, many recipes for sloe gin — here's an easy one.

Pick your sloes from blackthorn hedges in October or November when they are most ripe — probably after the first frost.

1. Take a litre (2 pint) bottle of gin, and remove half of the liquid and store in a separate bottle.

2. Cut or prick the sloes and drop into the half-empty bottle so that they displace the remaining gin to near the top.

3. Add one wine glass of sugar (approx 150 g/5½ oz).

4. All you have to do now is turn or agitate the bottle daily for a week, then weekly for a month or two . . . by which time it will be ready to drink (but it is really best kept until the next winter).

STRAWBERRIES

ICED STRAWBERRY TEA

The tea is already sweet from the strawberries; so if you like, you can cut back on the sugar a bit.

You will need: **Makes about 1.4 litres (2½ pints)**
   225 g (8 oz) fresh ripe strawberries
   900 ml (1½ pints) brewed tea, cooled
   55–115 g (2–4 oz) caster sugar (depending on how sweet
      you want the tea)
   60 ml (2 fl oz) freshly-squeezed lemon juice

1. Reserve 4–5 of the most perfect berries for the garnish.

2. Purée the remaining strawberries in a blender or food processor until smooth.

3. If you are a purist, strain the puréed berries to remove the seeds (optional).

4. In a jug, mix together the strawberries, tea, lemon juice, and desired amount of sugar. Chill until you are ready to serve.

5. Serve with ice and the reserved berries.

STRAWBERRY BREAD

This delicious, light tea bread is perfect on its own, simply spread with butter and a little cinnamon or lightly slicked with strawberry jam. Feel free to experiment with other berry and jam combinations — I have used mixed berries and raspberry jam, blueberries and gooseberry jam and cranberries with berries and cherries jam. You can either make it in the breadmaker, as I do, or follow the traditional breadmaking method.

You will need: **Makes one 675 g (1½ lb) loaf**
   120 ml (4 fl oz) milk
   120 ml (4 fl oz) water
   1 large egg, beaten
   3 tablespoons melted butter
   4 tablespoons orange marmalade
   1 teaspoon salt
   450 g (1 lb) strong white bread flour
   1¼ teaspoons fast action yeast*
   100 g (3½ oz) sun-dried strawberries,
     (cut into quarters if whole)

Breadmaker method:
Put the ingredients into the breadmaker pan in the order specified for your particular breadmaker. Set to the basic white programme. Add the berries when directed. When the baking cycle has finished, carefully shake the loaf from the bread pan onto a wire rack to cool.

Traditional baking method:
Put the flour, strawberries and salt into a bowl and sprinkle the yeast over. (If you want your bread to prove faster, use 2 teaspoons of yeast.) Mix to a soft dough with the marmalade, butter, egg, milk and water. Turn out onto a floured work surface and knead for 10 minutes. Shape as desired and put into an appropriate greased tin. Leave to prove until double in size. Place in an oven preheated to 220°C (425°F/Gas Mark 7) and immediately turn the oven down to 200°C (400°F/Gas Mark 6) and bake for 25–30 minutes until the loaf sounds hollow when tapped on the bottom. Turn out onto a wire rack and cool before slicing.

THE ULTIMATE STRAWBERRY SHAKE

What could be better than a fresh strawberry shake made with plump, ripe berries? This one is loaded with berries and premium ice cream, and topped with whipped cream.

You will need: **Makes 2 shakes**
>   280 g (10 oz) fresh, ripe strawberries
>   115 g (4 oz) caster sugar
>   600 ml (1 pint) premium vanilla ice cream
>   150 ml (5 fl oz) single cream
>   Sweetened whipped cream for topping

1. Chill the blender container and glasses.

2. Rinse, trim and slice the berries. Sprinkle the sugar on the berries and let them sit at room temperature for two hours or overnight in the refrigerator.

3. Make the shakes one at a time. Place half the strawberries and half the ice cream in a blender plus half the juice from the berries. Purée until smooth. Add half the single cream and blend again.

4. Pour the shake into the chilled glass, and refrigerate while you make the second shake. Top with the sweetened whipped cream.

FROZEN STRAWBERRY CREAM

You will need: **Serves 6–8**
>   350 g (12 oz) fresh strawberries, sliced
>   900 g (2 lb) low-fat vanilla yogurt
>   2 tablespoons caster sugar
>   6–8 strawberries with stems

1. Purée half of the strawberries in a food processor or blender.

2. Tip into a bowl and mix with the yogurt.

3. Toss the remaining strawberries with the sugar and stir into the yogurt.

4. Freeze in an ice-cream maker following the manufacturer's instructions or freeze in a shallow container until almost solid, cut into 2.5-cm (1-inch) cubes and whizz in a food processor until smooth. Garnish with a stemmed strawberry.

SZECHUAN PEPPER

CHINESE FIVE-SPICE POWDER

According to Chinese culinary tradition, all five flavours (salty, bitter, sweet, sour and pungent) are provided by five-spice powder. It is often extended to six or even seven spices with the addition of ginger, cardamom, or liquorice. Use it sparingly in marinades and to season meat or poultry before grilling or roasting.

You will need: **Makes about 60 ml (4 tablespoons)**
- 6 whole star anise
- 1 tablespoon Szechuan peppercorns
- 1 tablespoon fennel seeds
- 2 teaspoons whole cloves
- 2 teaspoons ground cinnamon

Combine all of the ingredients in a spice grinder and process to a fine powder.

WHITECURRANTS

WHITECURRANT WINE

This is another ambitious recipe using berries to make wine. If you are new to winemaking, to find out about some of these lesser-known ingredients or methods, either go to a shop that caters to home winemaking, or look them up on the Internet.

You will need:
> 1.8–2.25 kg (4–5) lb fresh, ripe whitecurrants
> 1.1 kg (2½ lb) granulated sugar
> 3 litres (5¼ pints) water
> 1 crushed Campden tablet
> 1 teaspoon yeast nutrient
> 1 packet Burgundy wine yeast

1. Put the fruit in the primary fermentation vessel and crush. Add 1 litre (1¾ pints) of water, crushed Campden tablet and yeast nutrient and stir. Meanwhile, add half the sugar to 1 litre (1¾ pints) of water and bring to the boil while stirring to dissolve. Add to primary and stir. Cover and allow to cool overnight.

2. Add the activated yeast, re-cover, and stir daily for 5–6 days. Strain through a nylon sieve and transfer the juice to sanitised secondary and fit airlock. Bring another litre (1¾ pints) of water to the boil and stir in remainder of the sugar until dissolved. When cool, add to secondary vessel and refit airlock.

3. After 3 additional days, top up with water, refit airlock and set aside until fermentation stops. Rack, top up and refit airlock.

4. After 60 days, rack again, top up and refit airlock. After an additional 60 days, rack into bottles and age 6 months before tasting.

[Adapted from H.E. Bravery's *Amateur Wine-Making*]

MIXED BERRY RECIPES

BERRIES WITH RICOTTA CRÈME

You will need: **Serves 6–8**

    450 g (1 lb) strawberries
    450 g (1 lb) raspberries
    450 g (1 lb) blackberries
    675 g (1½ lb) ricotta cheese
    55 g (2 oz) icing sugar
    85 g (3 oz) plain chocolate, finely chopped
    Rind of ½ orange
    85 g (3 oz) flaked almonds, toasted
    6–8 sprigs mint

1. Combine the berries in a large bowl.

2. Place the ricotta cheese and icing sugar in a food processor and whizz until smooth, or beat with a handheld electric mixer. Stir in the remaining ingredients.

3. To serve, spoon the berries into a dessert glass and top with a portion of the ricotta crème. Garnish with a sprig of mint.

BUMBLEBERRY BLACK BOTTOM PIE

There is no such thing as a bumbleberry. It's a joke perpetrated by two Californian ladies. But this pie isn't a joke at all. It's divine.

You will need:
115 g (4 oz) plain chocolate
2 tablespoons orange juice
4 large eggs, separated
115 g (4 oz) granulated sugar
½ teaspoon cinnamon
Pinch of salt
350 g (12 oz) mixed berries (blueberries, blackberries, raspberries)
3 tablespoons granulated sugar
240 ml (8 fl oz) double cream whipped with 2 tablespoons icing sugar and 2 tablespoons orange or berry liqueur (optional)
Shaved chocolate (optional)

1. Preheat the oven to 180°C (350°F/Gas Mark 4). Butter a 25 cm (10-inch) pie tin.

2. Melt the chocolate with the orange juice in a microwaveable jug. Stir until smooth and leave to cool.

3. Beat the egg yolks with the sugar in a bowl until very thick and pale in colour. Add the cinnamon and melted chocolate, beating slowly until blended.

4. Whisk the egg whites with the salt until stiff. Add the egg whites one-third at a time to the chocolate mixture, folding in gently with a spatula. Pour the mixture into the pie tin, level with the spatula, and bake for about 25 minutes. Allow to cool. As the crust cools it will sink in the centre, forming a shell.

5. In large bowl, toss the berries with the sugar. Fill the cooled pie shell with the berry mixture. Spread with whipped cream and sprinkle with shaved chocolate, if using.

FRUIT AND NUT SNACK BARS

If you're looking for some easy and wholesome snacks to make for your children, think inside the box — the cereal box. A number of cereals contain whole grains that are packed with antioxidants, vitamins, minerals and fibre. The grains help to keep bodies healthy, help maintain a healthy heart and can even help manage weight.

These no-fuss bars require no baking. Start with a snack mix made with puffed wheat, oat or rice cereal, stir in the syrup and press them into a pan. The tasty treat is easy to transport and the bar shape makes this snack ready to grab and go. They're a good breakfast treat when there's no time to eat, a great addition to lunches, or a good 'anytime' snack.

You will need: **Makes 36 bars**

225 g (8 oz) puffed wheat, oat or rice cereal
115 g (4 oz) dried mixed berries, chopped
55 g (2 oz) sunflower seeds
55 g (2 oz) dry-roasted peanuts
170 g (6 oz) brown sugar
120 ml (4 fl oz) golden syrup
4 tablespoons peanut butter
1 teaspoon vanilla essence

1. Spray a 33 x 23 cm (13 x 9-inch) tin with cooking spray. In a large bowl, mix together the cereal, berries, sunflower seeds and peanuts. Set aside.

2. In a saucepan, stir together the brown sugar, golden syrup and peanut butter. Bring to the boil over a medium-high heat, stirring constantly. Boil for 1 minute. Remove from the heat and stir in the vanilla essence.

3. Pour the syrup over the cereal mix, stirring until evenly coated. Press mixture firmly into the prepared tin. Cool completely, about 30 minutes. For bars, cut into 9 rows by 4 rows. Store in a tightly covered container.

FRUITS OF THE FOREST COFFEE CAKE

This is a most excellent cake. Everyone who has ever tasted it looks for an excuse to come for coffee in the hope that this cake will be on offer! It's always different because I use the berries I have to hand at the time. Sometimes I throw in chopped almonds, walnuts or pecans instead of marzipan. It always turns out well.

You will need: **Makes one 25 cm (10-inch) cake**

  225 g (8 oz) sunflower margarine
  600 g (1 lb 5 oz) caster sugar
  1½ teaspoons vanilla essence
  ½ teaspoon almond essence
  4 large eggs
  400 g + 1 teaspoon (14 oz + 1 teaspoon) plain flour
  75 g (2½ oz) oat bran
  2 teaspoons baking powder
  1 teaspoon bicarbonate of soda
  2 tablespoons ground cinnamon
  450 g (1 lb) low-fat cranberry and raspberry (or vanilla) yogurt
  225 g (8 oz) mixed dried fruit*, coarsely chopped
  55 g (2 oz) grated marzipan

1. Preheat the oven to 180°C (350°F/Gas Mark 4). Lightly grease a 25 cm (10-inch) tube pan.

2. In a large mixing bowl cream together the margarine and 225 g (8 oz) of the sugar, until fluffy. Add the vanilla and almond essences and the eggs, one at a time, beating well after each addition.

3. Combine the flour, oat bran, baking powder, bicarbonate of soda and cinnamon in another bowl. Add alternately with the yogurt to the egg mixture, beating just enough to keep the batter smooth.

4. In another bowl, combine the remaining sugar, dried fruit and marzipan.

5. Spoon one-fourth of the batter into the prepared pan, sprinkle with one-third of the berry mixture and repeat

layers twice more. End with the batter, smoothing the top. Shake the pan to settle the ingredients.

6. Bake for 70 minutes, until a toothpick inserted into the centre of the cake comes out clean. Remove from the oven and cool in the pan for 10 minutes, then remove from the pan and continue to cool on a wire rack.

Because this cake is so large, you might want to freeze half of it. I usually store one half in the refrigerator and one half in the freezer.

*Choose from cranberries, blueberries, raspberries, cherries, goji berries or strawberries.

TRIPLE BERRY FREEZE

You will need: **Makes 4 servings**
    500 ml (16 fl oz) sparkling water, chilled
    4 scoops lemon sorbet
    55 g (2 oz) frozen raspberries
    55 g (2 oz) frozen blueberries
    55 g (2 oz) frozen blackberries
    1 tablespoon honey

Place sparkling water and sorbet in a blender, and process until well-blended. Add the raspberries, blueberries, blackberries and honey; process until the mixture is smooth.

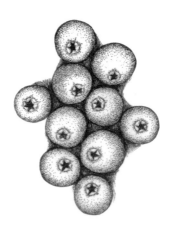

LAYERED FRUIT SALAD

You will need: **Serves 6–8**

   2 medium crisp red apples, cored and chopped
   225 g (8 oz) fresh blueberries
   225 g (8 oz) fresh strawberries, sliced
   225 g (8 oz) seedless green grapes, cut in half
   2 tablespoons freshly-squeezed lemon juice
   1 teaspoon grated lemon rind
   225 g (8 oz) fromage frais or cream cheese, softened
   240 ml (8 fl oz) whipping cream
   55 g (2 oz) icing sugar
   55 g (2 oz) chopped walnuts

1. In a large glass bowl layer half of the fruit in the order given.

2. In a separate bowl mix the cheese, lemon juice and lemon rind.

3. In another bowl whip the cream, just until soft peaks form; add the icing sugar and whip to form stiff peaks. Fold the cheese mixture and whipped cream mixture together.

4. Spread half the cream mixture over the fruit and repeat the layers. Sprinkle with walnuts. Serve immediately or store, covered, in the refrigerator.

A FEW TIPS:
Feel free to substitute your favourite summer fruits: other berries, peaches, cherries, for example. Don't use melons — they are too juicy. Be sure to drain the fruit well for a few minutes after chopping, or you'll end up with a puddle at the bottom of the dish after a few hours.

Skincare
Recipes

INDEX OF RECIPES

BLUEBERRY TONIC MASK

Soothing and nourishing for the face, make this mask the day you plan to use it.

Makes enough for one treatment
    3 tablespoons steamed, crushed blueberries
    115 g (4 oz) plain yogurt

1. Purée the ingredients in a blender at low speed until well mixed and fluffy. If it is too runny after blending, refrigerate for 1 hour.

2. Apply to the face and neck, taking care to avoid the eyes. Leave on for 15–20 minutes.

3. Rinse off with lukewarm water. Pat your skin dry with a soft towel.

CRANBERRY LIP GLOSS

Makes about 15 g (½ oz)
    1 tablespoon almond oil
    10 fresh cranberries
    1 teaspoon honey
    1 teaspoon petroleum jelly (optional, for more shine)

1. Mix together all the ingredients in a clean glass microwaveable container.

2. Heat in the microwave until the mixture just begins to boil (1-2 minutes). Stir well and gently mash the berries. Set aside for 5 minutes.

3. Strain the mixture through a fine sieve to remove all the cranberry solids. Stir and allow to cool completely. When cool, spoon into a clean container.

4. Apply to the lips as desired.

STRAWBERRY FOOT EXFOLIANT

Makes one treatment
- 8 ripe strawberries
- 3 tablespoons coarse sea salt
- 2 tablespoons olive oil

1. In a bowl, lightly mash the strawberries. Add the salt and olive oil. Don't overblend or the mixture will be too runny. If this happens, put it into the refrigerator for 1 hour.

2. To use, rub over your feet to smooth any rough skin. Rinse with lukewarm water and pat dry with a soft towel.

STRAWBERRY SKIN REFINING MASK

- 85 g (3 oz) very ripe strawberries
- 4 tablespoons cornflour

1. In a bowl, mix the strawberries and cornflour together to make a paste.

2. Apply to the face, avoiding the delicate area around the eyes. Leave on for 30 minutes.

3. Rinse off with cool water and pat dry with a soft towel.